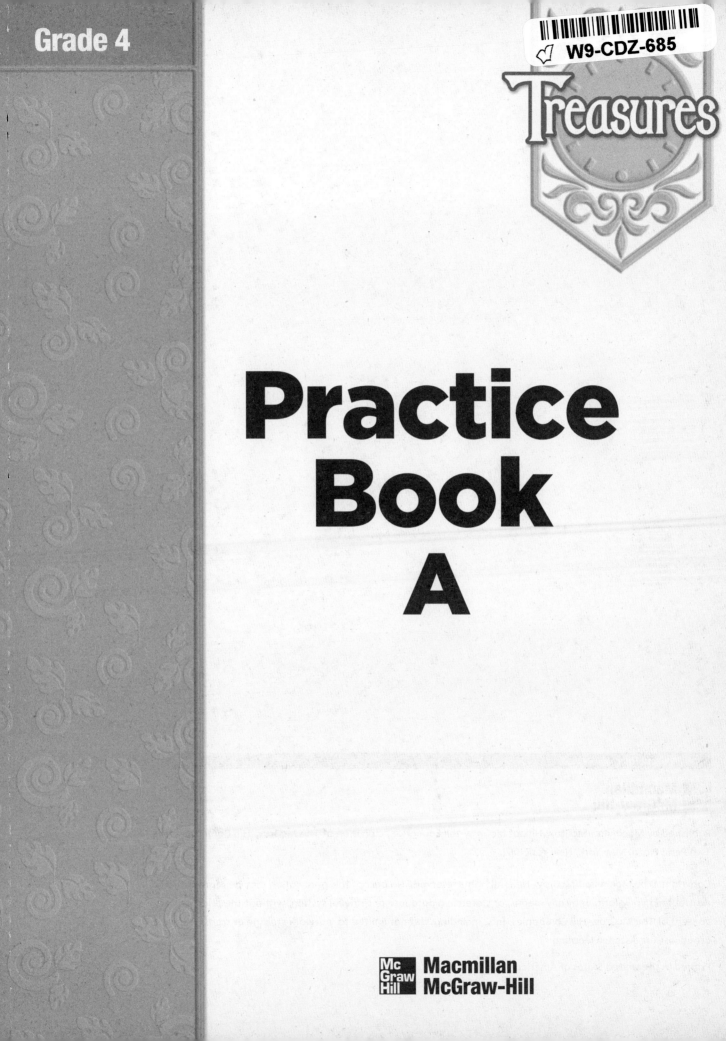

Treasures

Practice
Book
A

Macmillan
McGraw-Hill

B

The *McGraw·Hill* Companies

**Macmillan
McGraw-Hill**

Published by Macmillan/McGraw-Hill, of McGraw-Hill Education, a division of The McGraw-Hill Companies, Inc.,
Two Penn Plaza, New York, New York 10121.

Printed in the United States of America

7 8 9 10 066 09

Contents

Unit 2 • Take a Stand

Unit 3 • Making a Difference

© Macmillan/McGraw-Hill

v

Unit 4 • Viewpoints

Unit 5 • Relationships

© Macmillan/McGraw-Hill

Unit 6 • Discovery

© Macmillan/McGraw-Hill

Read the vocabulary words. Write the correct word in each sentence below.

| allergies | assignments | suspicious | accuse |
| consideration | consume | evidence | |

1. Maria sneezed because she has _____.

2. Andre wrote down his _____ at school so he could remember them.

3. I didn't want to _____ him of taking my lunch.

4. I made up my mind not to _____ all of the popcorn at once.

5. I became _____ when I saw that my dog had crumbs on his face.

6. I thought he had eaten my lunch, but I didn't have any

    _____ to prove it.

7. I gave her idea careful _____ before I decided I liked it.

Write a sentence using one of the vocabulary words.

8. _____

_____

_____

_____

A story has a **problem** and a **solution**.
The **problem** is what the main character has to solve.
The **solution** is what the character does to solve the problem.

Read the passage. Then answer the questions that follow.

"Hey, Mario," Juan said to his big brother. "This little brown dog followed me home from school. I think he's lost. How can I find his owner?"

"Did you check if the dog has a tag on its collar?" Mario asked.

Juan checked. The dog had no collar or tag.

When Juan's parents got home, he told them about the dog. They took the dog to the vet. "Sometimes a dog will have an i.d. chip under the skin. It will tell us who owns the dog. We can read it with a special reader," the vet said. Sure enough, the vet found a chip and called the dog's owner. The owner picked up her puppy right away.

Underline the answer to each question in the passage. Then write your own answer on the line.

1. What is Juan's problem? _____

_____

2. What is one thing that Juan tried that did not work? _____

_____

3. What did Juan's parents to do help him? _____

_____

4. How is the problem solved? _____

_____

© Macmillan/McGraw-Hill

At Home: Ask the student to retell a familiar story or the plot of a TV show, explaining who the main character is, what the problem is, and how the problem is solved.

As you read *The Mystery of the Missing Lunch,* fill in the Problem and Solution Chart.

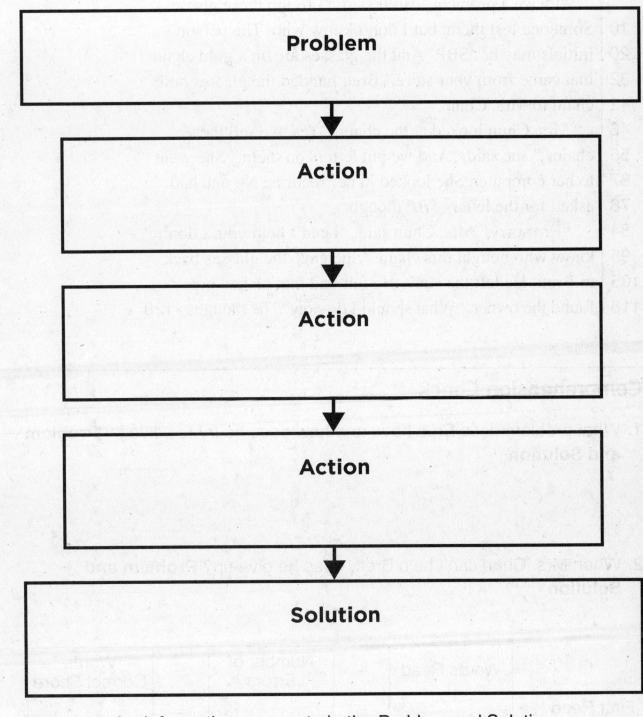

Problem

↓

Action

↓

Action

↓

Action

↓

Solution

How does the information you wrote in the Problem and Solution Chart help you to analyze *The Mystery of the Missing Lunch*?

 At Home: Have the student use the chart to retell the story.

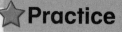
Name _____

As I read, I will pay attention to end punctuation in each sentence.

	"I have a problem," Brett said. "I found these glasses.
10	Someone lost them, but I don't know who. The person's
20	initials may be 'SBP.' And the glasses are on a gold chain
32	that came from your store." Brett handed the glasses and
42	chain to Mrs. Chun.
46	Mrs. Chun looked at the chain. "Yes, we sell these
56	chains," she said. "And we put letters on them." She went
67	to her computer. She looked in her records. No one had
78	asked for the letters *SBP* though.
84	"I'm sorry," Mrs. Chun said. "I can't help you. I don't
95	know who bought this chain." She gave the glasses back
105	to Brett. He left the store. He felt bad that he had not
118	found the owner. "What should I do now?" he thought. 128

Comprehension Check

1. What problem does Brett have and how does he try to solve it? **Problem and Solution**

2. When Mrs. Chun can't help Brett, does he give up? **Problem and Solution**

	Words Read	−	Number of Errors	=	Words Correct Score
First Read		−		=	
Second Read		−		=	

4 The Mystery of the Missing Lunch
Grade 4/Unit 4

At Home: Help the student read the passage, paying attention to the goal at the top of the page.

Name _____

> **Charts** are a good way to show information. There are **rows** that go across a chart. There are **columns** that go up and down in a chart.

Each day, the Mystery Store put different items on sale. For example, on Friday, the store featured the game "Where Is It?" and the puzzle "Maze."

The Mystery Store Sale Items

	Games	**Puzzles**
Thursday	Clue	Secret Word
Friday	Where Is It?	Maze
Saturday	Secret Hunt	500-piece puzzle

Circle your answer to each question in the chart. Then write your answer on the line.

1. If you wanted to buy a Secret Word puzzle on sale, which day would you go to the Mystery Store? _____

2. What kind of game was on sale on Saturday? _____

3. On what day was the 500-piece puzzle on sale? _____

4. What game could you get on sale on Thursday? _____

Answer the following questions.

5. How many games in all were on sale during the sale? ____

6. Which game or puzzle would you like to buy? When would you buy it?

_____

At Home: Together, create a chart that lists the days of the week. Add two column heads "Tasks" and "Play." Make up a schedule of what chores and what kinds of games the student will play each day.

The Mystery of the Missing Lunch
Grade 4/Unit 1

5

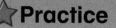
A dictionary can help you understand the meanings of **unfamiliar words**.

Look at the dictionary entry below.

part of
speech   definition
↓   ↓

entry word → material *noun.* The substance or substances from which
       something is made. *We needed more* material *to finish*
       building the shed.
           ↑
       example

Circle the correct answer to each question.

1. The entry word for the above is:

   a. material

   b. noun

2. If you wanted to see the word being used, where would you look?

   a. in the definition

   b. in the example

3. The word *material* is what part of speech?

   a. noun

   b. substance

4. To find what a word means, look at the:

   a. part of speech

   b. definition

© Macmillan/McGraw-Hill

 At Home: Look for unfamiliar words in books or magazines.
Look them up in the dictionary.

Name _____

Say the word **mat**. Listen to the **a** sound. In this word, **a** stands for a **short vowel sound**. When a vowel is between two consonants, it usually has a short sound.
These are the short vowel sounds:

a as in **hat**   **e** as in **bet**   **i** as in **mill**

o as in **lot**   **u** as in **sum**

Look at the short-vowel words below. Use them to complete the sentences that follow.

duck   dock   bit   bet   run   rim   pin   pen   hid   had

1. The _____ quacked loudly.

2. The letter was written with a blue _____ .

3. The dog _____ down hard on the bone.

4. I put the box in a secret spot and forgot where I _____ it.

5. The boat was tied up to the _____ .

6. The mystery book was the best one I _____ .

 At Home: Read a book with the student. As you read, have him or her identify short-vowel sounds.

The Mystery of the Missing Lunch
Grade 4/Unit 4
 7

| climate | silken | lumbering | swallows |
| lurk | shimmer | eerie | |

Use a vocabulary word from the list to complete each sentence.

1. When it eats, a snake opens its jaws wide and _____ its dinner whole.

2. The empty street with its dark shadows looked _____.

3. My sister's hair is _____ and soft after she washes and dries it.

4. On a clear night, the moon and stars _____ brightly in the sky.

5. Suddenly the bear cubs began _____ after their mother.

6. The _____ of the desert is dry and hot.

7. Our dogs often _____ near the table at mealtime, hoping for a treat.

Write three sentences, each using one of the vocabulary words.

8. _____

_____

9. _____

_____

10. _____

_____

© Macmillan/McGraw-Hill

Name _____

> To find the **main idea** of a text, ask yourself what the text you are reading is mostly about. Look for supporting **details** that can tell you more about the main idea.

Read the following passage.

There is little water in the desert, and it is very hot. Still, people have found a way to live in the desert. Fewer people live in deserts than in most other places. Towns are often isolated and far from other communities. They bring in water from other places. Many residents have air conditioning to keep them cool and comfortable. Television, telephones, and the Internet keep them from being isolated. It is also fairly easy to travel to other cities by car or plane.

Circle the letter of the correct response.

1. What is the main idea of this passage?

a. People have found ways to live in the desert.

b. Many people have air conditioning.

2. Which is a supporting detail?

a. There are towns and cities in the deserts.

b. There is little water in a desert.

Underline a detail to answer each question. Then write your answer on the lines.

3. How do people live in the desert?

_____

4. What is a detail that does not tell about the main idea?

_____

At Home: Together, read a paragraph in a favorite book. Discuss what the main idea might be. Find supporting details.

A Walk in the Desert
Grade 4/Unit 1

 9

© Macmillan/McGraw-Hill

Name _____

As you read *A Walk in the Desert*, fill in the Main Idea Chart.

Main Ideas	Details

How does the information you wrote in the Main Idea Chart help you
to summarize *A Walk in the Desert*?

 At Home: Have the student use the chart to retell the story.

As I read I will pay attention to tempo.

	Animals have many adaptations that help them survive
8	in a hot, dry **climate.** An adaptation may have to do with
20	an animal's body. A desert animal's feet may be built in a
32	way that keeps it from sinking into the sand. An adaptation
43	may have to do with an animal's behavior. For example,
53	many desert animals are active at night when the air is cool.
65	One such animal is a lizard called the thorny devil. The
76	thorny devil drinks dew that falls on its back. Grooves
86	extend along its body. The grooves lead water into the
96	thorny devil's mouth. It catches rain the same way. 105

Comprehension Check

1. What is the main idea of the first paragraph? **Main Idea and Details**

2. Name some details about the adaptation of the thorny devil. **Main Idea and Details**

	Words Read	–	Number of Errors	=	Words Correct Score
First Read		–		=	
Second Read		–		=	

At Home: Help the student read the passage, paying attention to the goal at the top of the page.

A Walk in the Desert
Grade 4/Unit 1

11

Assonance occurs when the same or similar vowel sounds are repeated in two or more words grouped closely together. Assonance is often found in poems. For example, *light shines, wild.* A **metaphor** compares two different objects or ideas. For example, *a wet snake curving through the land* can be used to describe a river.

Read the following poem. Look for words that have similar vowel sounds. Also look for a metaphor. Then answer the questions that follow.

The Hawk

The hawk
Free and easy
Flies down to the green tree
A silent soldier it sits and
Watches.

1. Underline words that have the long *e* sound, such as *breeze* or *steal.*

   Write them on the line. _____

2. Circle the word pairs that are an example of assonance.

   a. flies, silent

   b. down, sits

3. To what is the hawk compared in this poem?
   Circle the correct answer.

   a. a green tree

   b. a soldier

 At Home: Choose a word and see how many words the student can name that have the same vowel sound.

Name _____

> A **context clue** can help you figure out the meaning of a word you
> don't know. Sometimes nearby words help to explain the meaning
> of the unfamiliar word. For example:
>
> Reptiles, <u>such as snakes and lizards</u>, are found in the desert.

**Underline the words that help to explain the word in bold type.
Then circle the letter of the meaning that matches the word in
bold type.**

1. Some **regions** of the world, such as deserts and high mountains, can be
   very hot or very cold.

   a. places   **b.** cities

2. In the dry time of year, the river was as **shallow** as a ditch or puddle.

   a. not deep   **b.** shiny

3. Roadrunners don't stay **aloft**, gliding like a hawk or an eagle does, for
   very long.

   a. feathered   **b.** in the sky

4. Foxes raise their young in **dens**, built snugly in holes in the ground or in
   fallen trees.

   a. small, cozy places   **b.** parks

5. Scientists use **devices** such as thermometers to measure heat in the
   desert.

   a. animals   **b.** machines

At Home: Give the student sentences that have an
unfamiliar word and one or more examples related to the
word. Ask the student to guess the meaning of the word.

A Walk in the Desert
Grade 4/Unit 1

13

© Macmillan/McGraw-Hill

Name _____

Say the words *clay, gate,* and *bail.* You will hear the long *a* sound in each word.

The long *a* sound can be spelled in different ways:

ay   pl<u>ay</u>, st<u>ay</u>

ai   m<u>ai</u>l, r<u>ai</u>n

a_e   h<u>a</u>t<u>e</u>, n<u>a</u>m<u>e</u>

ei   w<u>ei</u>gh, <u>ei</u>ght

ea   br<u>ea</u>k, st<u>ea</u>k

Circle the words with the long *a* sound. Then use each long *a* word in a sentence.

1. that   pale   lawn

_____

2. claim   spat   ladder

_____

3. fallen   clay   grand

_____

4. break   what   star

_____

5. claw   flat   plain

_____

6. when   weigh   white

_____

© Macmillan/McGraw-Hill

At Home: Look through a book with the student and ask him or her to identify words with the long *a* sound.

Name _____

A. Write the vocabulary word that best fits in each blank.

| journey | wildlife | natural | roamed | completed |

1. If a bear wandered about in an area inside the park, you could say that

   it _____.

2. What would you call a trip around the world? _____

3. What is another word for finished? _____

4. What word can you use to describe an environment that people haven't

   changed in any way? _____

5. What is another word for the animals that live in our national parks?

   _____

B. Write sentences using three of the vocabulary words above.

1. _____

   _____

2. _____

   _____

3. _____

   _____

Name _____

> The **main idea** of a paragraph is its most important idea.
> **Details** in the paragraph help support the main idea.

Read the paragraph below. Then answer the questions that follow.

The wolves brought to Yellowstone National Park had a lot to learn.
They had been taken from their pack, or family group. A wolf pack has
"family" rules. What were the rules in their new pack? And who would
they play with?

What was their territory, or area? After all, wolves have to keep
intruders away, just as people close the doors of their homes to keep
intruders away. What kinds of animal would they hunt for food?

Wolves talk with one another by howling in "song fests." How would
they learn the new "language?" Yes, these wolves had a lot to learn!

1. Underline the answer that best describes the main idea of
   this passage:

   a. Wolves are very interesting.

   b. The wolves brought to Yellowstone National Park
   had a lot to learn.

List three supporting details below.

2. _____

   _____

3. _____

   _____

4. _____

   _____

16

Animals Come Home to Our
National Parks • **Grade 4/Unit 1**

At Home: Read a brief nonfiction selection with the student.
Then ask him or her to identify the main idea of the selection
along with one or two details that support it.

Name _____

As you read *Animals Come Home to Our National Parks,*
fill in the Main Idea Chart.

Main Ideas	Details

How does the information you wrote in the Main Idea Chart help you
to summarize *Animals Come Home to Our National Parks*?

 At Home: Have the student use the chart to retell the story.

Animals Come Home to Our
National Parks • Grade 4/Unit 1

17

© Macmillan/McGraw-Hill

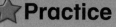
Name _____

As I read, I will pay attention to the pronunciation of vocabulary words and other difficult words.

	Isle Royale National Park is not easy to reach. There
10	are no bridges to this island park near Minnesota and
20	Michigan in Lake Superior. People must either fly or sail
30	to get there. But 18,000 people visit each year. Their
40	**journey** to the island is well worth the trouble.
49	People hike on Isle Royale's forest trails. They swim
58	in its lakes. They look at its waterfalls.
66	This park is a good place for **wildlife,** too. The animals
77	feel safe from humans in this park. They can eat the plants
89	that grow in the marshes and woods. The park is like a
101	**natural** zoo where all the animals manage to live with
111	each other. 113

Comprehension Check

1. What is the main idea in the first paragraph? **Main Idea and Details**

2. What details support the idea that the park is a good place for wildlife? **Main Idea and Details**

	Words Read	–	Number of Errors	=	Words Correct Score
First Read		–		=	
Second Read		–		=	

At Home: Help the student read the passage, paying attention to the goal at the top of the page.

Name _____

A **dictionary** is a book that provides information about words listed in alphabetical order. Each dictionary entry tells you how to spell the word, how to pronounce it, and what it means.

Read the dictionary entry and the box below. Answer the questions that follow.

park (pärk) n. **1.** enclosed land with wildlife owned by royalty. **2a.** land in or near a city or town used for recreation. **2b.** a natural area owned by the public. **3.** an enclosed stadium used for ball games.

> Main Entry: park
> Pronunciation: (pärk)
> Part of speech: *n. = noun*
> Definitions: 1, 2a, 2b, 3

1. What is the main entry? _____

2. Underline the correct pronunciation of *park*.

   a. park

   b. pärk

   c. perk

3. Which definition, or meaning, best fits the selection "Animals Come Home to Our National Parks"? _____

4. Which definition best fits a park with a playground in it? _____

5. According to this entry, what part of speech is *park*? _____

At Home: Look through a children's dictionary or other dictionary together. Guide him or her in identifying the different parts of each entry.

Animals Come Home to Our
National Parks • **Grade 4/Unit 1**

Name _____

When two words are put together to form one word, the new word is called a **compound word**.

Circle the compound word in each sentence. Write the two words that make up each compound word.

1. Juan, Ken and Ali were hiking in Yellowstone National Park.

Word parts: _____ + _____

2. Their backpacks were heavy with gear and food.

Word parts: _____ + _____

3. They set up camp by a freshwater lake.

Word parts: _____ + _____

4. Thunderheads built up in the sky.

Word parts: _____ + _____

5. Suddenly there was a downpour.

Word parts: _____ + _____

6. Everyone yanked his or her raincoat from a pack.

Word parts: _____ + _____

7. Nafeesa found five letters in her mailbox.

Word parts: _____ + _____

8. Ling watched the hammerhead shark at the aquarium.

Word parts: _____ + _____

© Macmillan/McGraw-Hill

At Home: Ask whether *basket* or *pencil* are compound words. Discuss why they are not.

Name _____

A long vowel has the same sound as its name.
The long *e* sound is spelled in different ways.
Here are three of the most common:
- *ee* as in *see*
- *ea* as in *seal*
- *ie* as in *thief*

Say the words below out loud to yourself. Circle those that have a long *e* sound.

1. deal

2. dent

3. relief

4. between

5. breathe

6. breath

When a single letter *e* comes at the end of a word, it is usually silent. You cannot hear the *e* when you say the word, but it can change the word's sound.

7. What word in the list on this page ends with a silent *e*? Write it here.

_____

8. How did the silent *e* change the sound of the word?

_____

 At Home: Look through some textbooks together. Point out words with long *e* sounds and ask your child to pronounce them. Together, discuss the words' spellings.

Name _____

| endless | universe | protested | realistic |
| sensible | astronaut | paralyzed | |

Read each clue. Then match each meaning with a vocabulary word.

1. everything in space _____

2. without a finish _____

3. making good sense _____

4. a traveler in space _____

5. argued against something _____

6. showing the way things really are _____

7. not able to move _____

8. Choose one of the vocabulary words above and use it in a sentence of your own.

_____

_____

© Macmillan/McGraw-Hill

The people (or animals) in a story are called **characters.**
The main character is the one on which the story focuses.
The **plot** of a story describes what happens to the characters
from beginning to end.
The **setting** of a story is where the story takes place.

Read the story below. Then answer the questions that follow.

Ricardo played basketball on an after-school team. They played in the
school gym. At first Ricardo tried to make a basket every time he had the
ball. Then he listened when his coach talked about working together to
win a game. The next time that the ball came to Ricardo, he passed it to
someone closer to the basket. Once when his teammate Alex passed the
ball to him, Ricardo saw that he could shoot it. He made a three-point
shot. Everyone on the team cheered, but Ricardo said, "Alex is the real
hero. He passed the ball to me instead of taking the shot himself."

1. Who are the characters in the story?

_____

2. Who is the main character? _____

3. What is the setting? _____

4. Circle the answer that best describes the character of Ricardo.

a. Ricardo has learned to value teamwork.

b. Ricardo always tries to make a basket.

 At Home: Read a familiar story. After the story help the
student decide who the main characters are and what they
are like.

The Astronaut and the Onion
Grade 4/Unit 1

 23

Name _____

As you read *The Astronaut and the Onion*, fill in the Character Web.

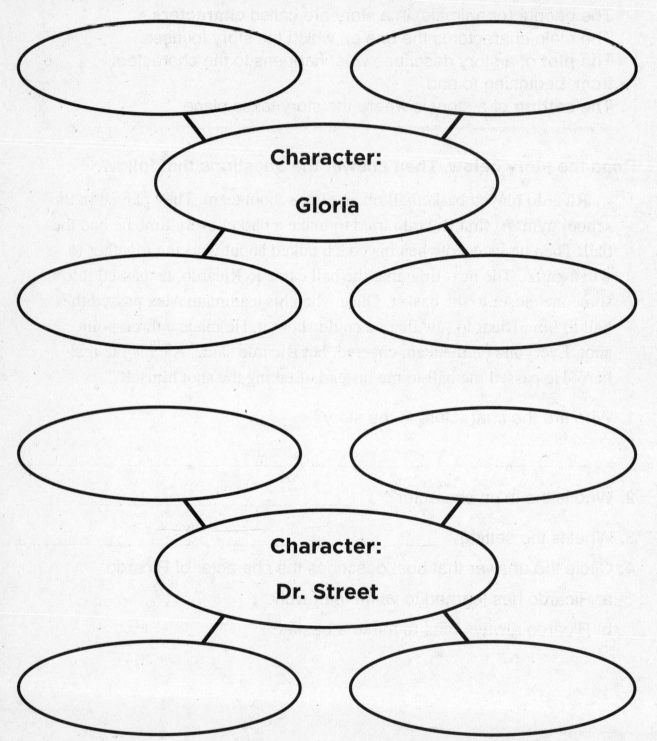

Character:

Gloria

Character:

Dr. Street

How does the information you wrote in the Character Web help you
analyze and make inferences about *The Astronaut and the Onion*?

At Home: Have the student use the chart to retell the story.

As I read, I will pay attention to pauses, stops, intonation, and the characters' words.

9	Chris Rogers was one cool kid. He could handle anything. At least that's what he wanted his mom to think.
20	Chris and his mom were parked in front of his new
31	friend Anton's apartment building. Chris wanted to go in
40	to see if Anton was home. And he didn't want his mom
52	coming with him. He was too big for that. And too cool.
64	"C'mon Mom," Chris begged. "Let me go in alone.
73	Please?"
74	"I don't know, honey," his mom said. "I'm not sure I
85	like the idea."
88	"But you've already met Anton and his mom. And I've
98	been to their place before." Chris hoped this would
107	convince her. 109

Comprehension Check

1. How would Chris feel if his mom went with him to Anton's apartment? **Character**

2. Why do you think Chris's mom doesn't want him to go to Anton's apartment by himself? **Character**

© Macmillan/McGraw-Hill

	Words Read	−	Number of Errors	=	Words Correct Score
First Read		−		=	
Second Read		−		=	

 At Home: Help the student read the passage, paying attention to the goal at the top of the page.

The Astronaut and the Onion
Grade 4/Unit 1

 25

Name _____

A **diagram** is a drawing that presents information. Some information Is easier to understand when it is shown in a diagram. A diagram may show something from the real world, but in a simpler form.

School
(1 mile)

Swimming
Pool
(4 miles)

Home

Library
(2 miles)

Mall
(7 miles)

Distances from Home

This diagram shows distances from home to different places nearby. Readers can compare the distances more easily than on a map.

Read the diagram to answer the questions below.

1. What is this diagram about? _____

_____

2. What does "1 mile" under School tell you? _____

_____

3. How far is it from home to the mall? _____

4. Is the library or the swimming pool closer to home? _____

_____

5. How much farther from home is the mall than the library? _____

_____

6. Town Hall is 5 miles from home. Put a dot on the diagram and label it.

At Home: Help the student make a diagram of the distances from your home to five locations in your area.

When you are reading and come to a word you don't know, a **dictionary** can tell you what the word means and how to say it.

> sensible (sen´ sə bəl) *adjective* 1. aware and responsive: *Ground control was* sensible *of the spaceship's problem.* 2. showing good sense: *Postponing the launch because of bad weather was a* sensible *decision.*

Look at this part of the entry: sen´ sə bəl. This is called the phonetic spelling. It shows you how to say the word.

The accent mark (´) after the first syllable shows that you stress that syllable.

Answer the questions in the spaces provided.

1. Write the actual spellings to match each phonetic syllable.

sen´ _____ sə _____ bəl _____

2. The word *sensible* has two meanings. Write the meaning that fits this sentence: " John was sensible of his mother's tiredness."

_____

3. Which meaning of *sensible* fits this sentence? "When she got to the store, Elena made sensible choices."

_____

4. What part of speech is *sensible?* Look after the phonetic spelling to find the correct answer. _____

At Home: With the student look up unfamiliar words in a dictionary. Use the phonetic spellings to find out how to say them.

The Astronaut and the Onion
Grade 4/Unit 1

27

Name _____

When two vowels are together in a word, often the first one says its sound and the second one is silent. For example, in the word *lie,* the *i* makes its **long sound** and the *e* is silent.

When a word has an *e* at the end, the vowel in that word is usually long. An example is the word *prime.*

When *i* is followed by *gh* or *ld,* it also has a long sound, as in *slight* and *mild.*

Finally, the long *i* sound can also be spelled with a *y,* as in *sly.*

Place each of the following long *i* words in the column where they belong:

drive, file, kite, wipe, pride, pry, shy, prime, mild, climb, sly, sigh, fright, inside, pies, die, spy, twice, slight

two vowels together	e at the end	i followed by gh or ld	y spelling

© Macmillan/McGraw-Hill

At Home: Look at a favorite story with the student. Choose a single page and ask the student to find and write down as many long-*i* words as possible.

**Read the vocabulary words. Then read the definitions.
Write the correct vocabulary word in each blank.**

raft	scattered	disgusted
nuzzle	downstream	cluttered

1. a simple boat made from logs _____

2. messy _____

3. grossed out _____

4. touch gently with your nose _____

5. went all over the place _____

6. the direction in which water is flowing _____

Write four sentences using a word from the box in each.

7. _____

_____

8. _____

_____

9. _____

_____

10. _____

_____

Name _____

> **Characters:** the people or animals in a story.
> The main characters are the ones that the story focuses on.
> **Setting:** where and when a story takes place
> **Plot:** what happens in a story

Read the story below. Then answer the questions that follow.

Janet and Jeremiah went on a bird walk in the park. They were bored, so they started making up bird calls.

At first they made the calls sound like real birds. Then they got carried away. They imitated cows, monkeys, and every other animal they could think of. They were sure surprised when all the dogs in the park started howling!

1. What is the setting of this story? _____

2. Who are the main characters? _____

3. Are the other characters people or animals? _____

4. List the events in the story. The first one is done for you.

Janet and Jeremiah go on a bird walk. _____

_____

_____

5. What are the events called? _____

6. Name the three story elements. _____

At Home: Have the student think of a favorite story, and tell you where it is set and who the main characters are.

Name _____

As you read *The Raft*, fill in the Setting Flow Chart.

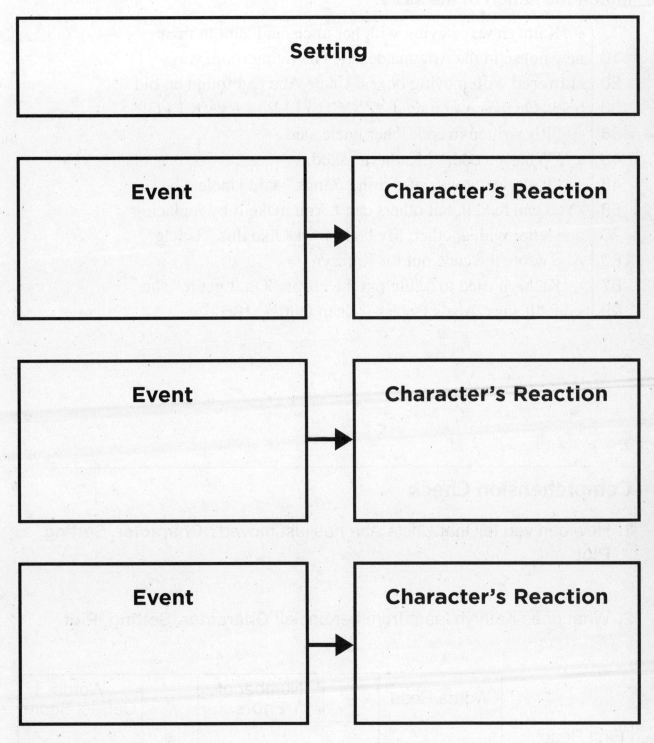

Setting

| **Event** | → | **Character's Reaction** |

| **Event** | → | **Character's Reaction** |

| **Event** | → | **Character's Reaction** |

How does the information you wrote in the Setting Flow Chart help
you to analyze and make inferences about *The Raft*?

At Home: Have the student use the chart to retell the story.

The Raft
Grade 4/Unit 1

31

© Macmillan/McGraw-Hill

As I read, I will pay attention to the pace and tempo and try to match the action of the story.

	Kathryn was staying with her uncle and aunt in their
10	new house in the Arizona desert. The living room was
20	**cluttered** with moving boxes. Uncle Abe had found an old
30	book. On the cover it read, "ZYV'H YLLP — PVVK LFG!"
36	"It's written in code," her uncle said.
43	"What's a code?" Kathryn asked.
48	"It's a secret way of writing things," said Uncle Abe.
58	"You can read it, but others can't. You make it by replacing
70	one letter with another. My code works like this." Uncle
80	Abe wrote the code out for Kathryn.
87	Kathryn tried to figure out the cover. "Oh, I get it," she
99	said. "It says 'Abe's Book — Keep Out!'" 106

Comprehension Check

1. How can you tell that Uncle Abe has just moved? **Character, Setting, Plot**

2. What does Kathryn learn from her uncle? **Character, Setting, Plot**

	Words Read	–	Number of Errors	=	Words Correct Score
First Read		–		=	
Second Read		–		=	

At Home: Help the student read the passage, paying attention to the goal at the top of the page.

Name _____

Maps can be very useful in helping you figure out where one place is in relation to another.
A **compass rose** has four points. It shows the cardinal directions.
The cardinal directions are north, south, east, and west.
The **map key** explains the symbols on the map. Each symbol stands for a different thing.

Answer each question.

1. ▭▬▭

   Would you drive or walk on this route?

   _____

2. Which symbol shows a place where you can find answers? Circle it.

3. What is this symbol called?

4. If you walked from Big Bluestem Pool to Nelson Pool, in which direction would you be traveling?

   north   east

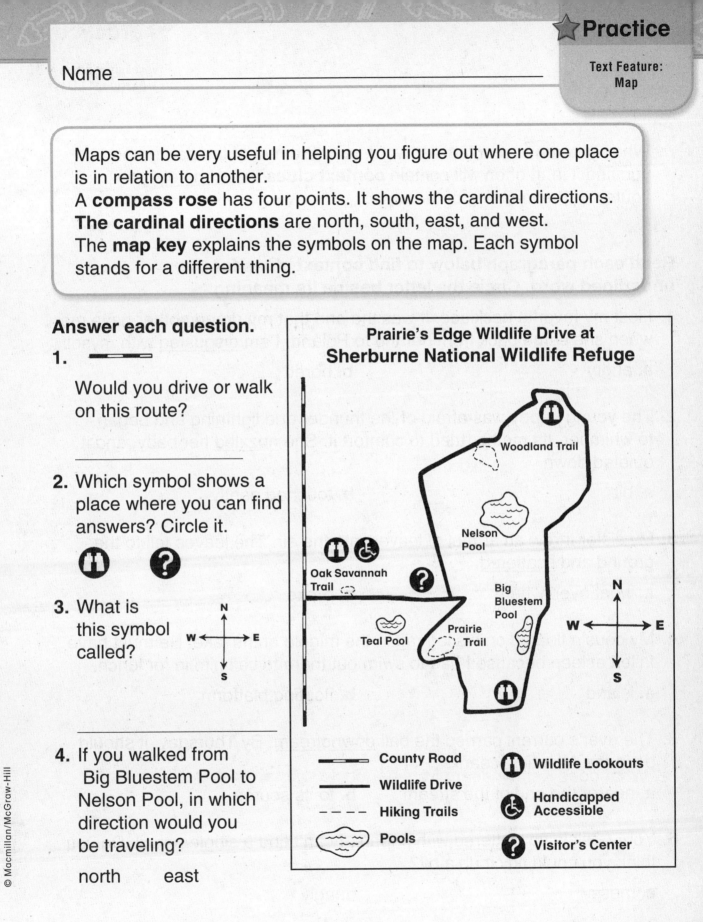

Prairie's Edge Wildlife Drive at
Sherburne National Wildlife Refuge

Woodland Trail
Nelson Pool
Oak Savannah Trail
Big Bluestem Pool
Teal Pool
Prairie Trail

▭▬▭ **County Road**   🔭 **Wildlife Lookouts**
——— **Wildlife Drive**   ♿ **Handicapped Accessible**
- - - **Hiking Trails**
〰️ **Pools**   ❓ **Visitor's Center**

 At Home: Ask the student to explain the different symbols on the map to you and locate them on the map.

When you read an unfamiliar word, read the rest of the paragraph you find it in. It often will contain **context clues** that can help you figure out the meaning of the word.

Read each paragraph below to find context clues for the underlined word. Circle the letter beside its meaning.

1. I lost my favorite necklace. It was the one that my grandmother gave me when she came back from her trip to Poland. I am <u>disgusted</u> with myself.

   a. angry **b.** bored

2. The young puppy was afraid of the thunder and lightning and began to whimper. Its mother tried to comfort it. She <u>nuzzled</u> her baby, and it quieted down.

   a. bit **b.** touched gently

3. My sister threw an armful of leaves into the air. The leaves fell to the ground and <u>scattered</u>.

   a. went everywhere **b.** broke

4. My cousin floated on his log <u>raft</u> in the middle of the lake. He must have fallen asleep because I had to swim out there to call him in for lunch.

   a. island **b.** floating platform

5. The river's current carried the ball <u>downstream</u>. By Thursday, it should be in the Atlantic Ocean!

   a. nearer the end of the stream **b.** to its source

6. Your desk is so <u>cluttered</u> with papers. I can't find a single pencil. Do you think you could tidy it up a bit?

   a. messy **b.** ugly

© Macmillan/McGraw-Hill

34 The Raft
Grade 4/Unit 1

At Home: Read a passage with the student. Have him or her identify unfamiliar words. Use context clues to interpret their meanings together.

Long o is the vowel sound in words like *rose*.
The long *o* sound can be spelled in different ways.
Say each word and pay attention to the different spellings.

o_e	oa	ow	o
stole	foam	flow	mold

Write each word from the box under the spelling category in which it belongs.

now	grow	told	pole	float	snow
more	rope	old	slow	moat	for

o_e	oa	ow	o
1. _____	3. _____	5. _____	8. _____
2. _____	4. _____	6. _____	9. _____
		7. _____	

Which words do not have the long o sound?

10. _____

11. _____

12. _____

 At Home: With the student, look for objects that are spelled with long *o*. See if he or she can spell each word.

 The Raft
Grade 4/Unit 1

 35

© Macmillan/McGraw-Hill

Name _____

A. Draw a line to match the word to its meaning.

1. suspicious   **a.** caused one's stomach to turn

2. silken   **b.** following the flow of a stream

3. natural   **c.** blame

4. downstream   **d.** not artificial

5. disgusted   **e.** soft and shiny

6. accuse   **f.** not trusting

B. Write words from the box to complete the letter.

| assignments | consume | journey | paralyzed |

Dear Professor Jones,

    I am writing to let you know what I need you to do next. The

_____ are dangerous, but I hope you will take them.

The matter is urgent.

    As you can see from the enclosed itinerary and map, you
will be exploring the Dark River. Whatever you do, don't

_____ the fruit of the Walla-Walla tree. It is poisonous and

will leave you completely _____.

    Enjoy as much of your _____ as you possibly can,
and write to me when you get back.
I do hope to hear from you again.

                           Sincerely,
                           Sam Snakely

© Macmillan/McGraw-Hill

Name _____

C. Read each question. Choose a word from the list to answer the question. Write your answer on the line.

| climate | lumbering | astronaut | cluttered | realistic |

1. When a story or a movie is true to life, what could you call it?

_____

2. If a big brown bear in the forest is moving toward you in a clumsy or

heavy way, how is it moving? _____

3. What do you call someone who travels into space? _____

4. If you tell people that a place is usually warm and rainy, what are you

telling them about? _____

5. If your desk had lots of papers all over it, how would it look?

_____

D. Write words from the box to complete the letter.

| eerie | roamed | wildlife | sensible | raft |

Dear Mr. Snakely,

I am back from my trip. I explored the Dark River on a

_____. I saw _____ in the jungle. But as

far as I _____, I never saw another person. It was very

_____. I can find no _____ explanation for

what might have happened to the people who lived there.

All the best,
Professor Jones

© Macmillan/McGraw-Hill

Name _____

Write the correct word after its meaning.

> | muttered | gaped | insult | snickering |
> | legendary | fluke | flinched | |

1. an accidental piece of good luck _____

2. shrank away from _____

3. laughing in a way that makes fun of someone _____

4. spoke unclearly in a soft voice _____

5. gazed in surprise with the mouth open _____

6. well-known or famous _____

7. something bad said to person _____

Answer each question with a vocabulary word.

8. Which word would you use to describe Babe Ruth?

   _____

9. Which word would you use to describe the way someone talked?

   _____

10. Which word would you use to describe mean people laughing?

    _____

An author always has a purpose when he or she writes.
- If you are reading fiction, the author's purpose is probably to **entertain.**
- If the story is nonfiction, the author's purpose is to **inform,** to tell you facts.
- If you read the author's opinion and the reasons for that opinion, the author's purpose is to **persuade.**

Read the story below and decide on the author's purpose.

Andrea rounded second and headed for third. She saw the third-base coach using his hands to tell her to slide. She slid, and got to third base safely.

She got up and dusted herself off. She was pleased to have a triple. Her friend Jorge was batting now. Andrea watched as the first pitch came in. He didn't swing, and it was called a ball. There were two outs, and the score was tied. A hit would win the game. On the very next pitch Jorge hit the ball hard, over the head of the shortstop and into left field. Andrea ran home easily.

1. Is this story nonfiction or fiction? _____

2. Circle the best description of the author's purpose for writing this story.
   a. to entertain   **b.** to inform   **c.** to persuade

Now read this story and decide on the author's purpose.

Willie Mays was born May 6, 1931, in Westfield, Alabama. He played baseball for the New York Giants, the San Francisco Giants, and the New York Mets. He was a skilled player in many ways, including hitting, fielding, throwing, and running bases. In 1951 he was named Rookie of the Year. His career statistics include 3,283 hits and 660 home runs. Willie Mays was elected to the Hall of Fame in 1979.

3. Is this story nonfiction or fiction? _____

4. What was the author's purpose in writing this story?
   a. to entertain   **b.** to inform   **c.** to persuade

At Home: Together, choose a favorite story. Discuss what the author's purpose was for writing that story.

As you read *Mighty Jackie*, fill in the Author's Purpose Map.

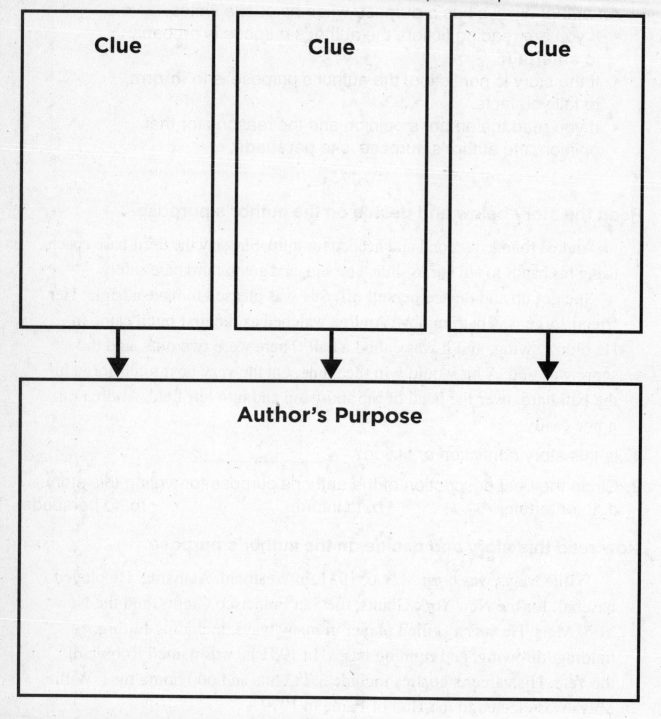

| Clue | Clue | Clue |

Author's Purpose

How does the information you wrote in the Author's Purpose Map
help you to analyze and make inferences about *Mighty Jackie*?

 At Home: Have the student use the chart to retell the story.

© Macmillan/McGraw-Hill

As I read, I will pay attention to pauses, stops, and intonation.

	Wilma Rudolph calmly walked to the starting line.
8	"Wilma!" the crowd yelled. It was 1960. She was running
17	in the Olympics.
20	People were shouting Wilma's name because she was
28	fast. They didn't care that she was African American or
38	poor. Here in Rome, Italy, Wilma was just another athlete
48	— a good one.
51	Wilma Rudolph won three gold medals at the 1960
59	Summer Olympics. That was amazing. Getting there at all
68	was even more amazing. When Wilma was a child, her
78	doctors said she would never walk.
84	Wilma worked hard. If she failed at something, she
93	worked harder. 95

Comprehension Check

1. How does the author want you to feel about Wilma Rudolph? **Author's Purpose**

2. How does the setting make Wilma feel calm? **Setting**

	Words Read	−	Number of Errors	=	Words Correct Score
First Read		−		=	
Second Read		−		=	

At Home: Help the student read the passage, paying attention to the goal at the top of the page.

Name _____

A table presents information, such as names, numbers, and facts, in an organized way. Tables are good to use when comparing information.

Look at this table from a sports almanac. It gives information about two of the greatest players in baseball history, Ted Williams and Hank Aaron.

	Ted Williams	Hank Aaron
Birthplace	San Diego, California	Mobile, Alabama
Nickname	The Splendid Splinter	Hammerin' Hank
Height	6 feet, 3 inches	6 feet
Weight	205 pounds	180 pounds
Batting average	.344	.305
Home runs	521	755

Use the table to answer these questions.

1. Which player was born in Alabama? _____

2. What was Ted Williams's nickname? _____

3. Which player was shorter? _____

4. Which player hit more home runs? _____

5. Which player had a higher batting average? _____

6. If you wanted to add another player to the chart, would you add a column

   or row? _____

At Home: Look through an almanac or an informational section of the newspaper. Discuss how information is presented. How would it be different in sentence form?

© Macmillan/McGraw-Hill

Name _____

Sometimes in a story you will find a word you do not know. When this happens, read the entire sentence or sentences nearby to see if there is a **description** that gives a clue to the meaning of that word. For example, if you read, "Their game uniforms were a *drab* color, a mixture of gray and beige," you know that drab must mean "dull."

Underline the correct meaning of the word in dark type. Use the clues in the sentence to help you.

1. My uncle always **exaggerated** how well he had played baseball in college. If he scored three runs in a game, he would claim to have scored six.

   a. said something was more than it was

   b. said something is less than it was

2. The Games Pitched statistic is the **cumulative** total of all the games a player has ever pitched.

   a. the amount so far

   b. important

3. The **relief** pitcher was called in when the regular pitcher got tired and began to make mistakes.

   a. tall

   b. replacement

4. The batter took a mighty swing. His bat got nowhere near the ball, and he **whiffed**.

   a. got a hit

   b. missed the ball

5. Bill tossed his **eephus** pitch gently, and the batter waited and waited for it to arrive.

   a. a slow pitch

   b. a fast pitch

 At Home: Read stories together, looking for words that are explained in context. Make a list of these words and the context clues that help define them.

The following words all have the **ch** sound:
      <u>ch</u>eap   ske<u>tch</u>ed   bran<u>ch</u>   hi<u>tch</u>
The sound can be spelled **ch** or **tch**.
The **ch** spelling can appear in the beginning, middle, or at the end of words. The **tch** spelling only appears in the middle or at the end of words.

Circle the *ch* or *tch* in the following words:

1. champ

2. watching

3. hitch

4. change

5. fetching

6. match

7. charge

8. rich

9. such

10. In which two words is the *ch* sound in the middle of the word?

_____

11. In which words is the *ch* sound at the end?

_____

12. In which words is the *ch* sound in the beginning?

_____

 At Home: Together, look through magazines or favorite stories to find 10 words with *ch* and *tch*. Make a list of them.

Name _____

Complete each definition by writing the correct word on the line provided.

overheard	opportunities	boycotts	citizen
unions	strikes	border	

1. someone who was born in a country or is allowed to live and

   vote there _____

2. a line between two countries _____

3. groups for people who do the same work _____

4. chances to do new things _____

5. these happen when a group of people all agree to stop working

   _____

6. listened to what other people talked about _____

7. these happen when people decide together not to buy something

   _____

8. Write a sentence using one of the words. _____

   _____

   _____

> Authors do not always directly state what is happening in a story. They also may not tell you exactly how characters are feeling. Sometimes you have to use clues in the story and what you know from your own experiences to help you **make inferences** about what's going on.

Read the story. Then make inferences to answer the questions that follow.

   Mei-Li stood next to her parents as they waited for their suitcases. Other people were rushing to catch their flights or meeting family and friends. The roar of airplanes overhead was very loud, and it never seemed to stop. Mei-Li tightly gripped her mother's hand. Everywhere she looked were strangers speaking English, a language she didn't understand.

   When they finally got their suitcases, Mei-Li yawned and rubbed her eyes. She couldn't wait to get to her uncle's house, where they were going to stay until her parents could find their own apartment. She wanted to lie down in a quiet place and go to sleep.

1. Where is Mei-Li at the beginning of the story? _____

2. What clues let you know where Mei-Li is? _____

_____

3. Why does Mei-Li grip her mother's hand? _____

4. How does Mei-Li feel at the end of the story? _____

5. How do you know how Mei-Li feels at the end? _____

_____

At Home: Reread a favorite story and make inferences based on the actions of the characters.

As you read *My Diary from Here to There*, fill in the Inferences Word Web.

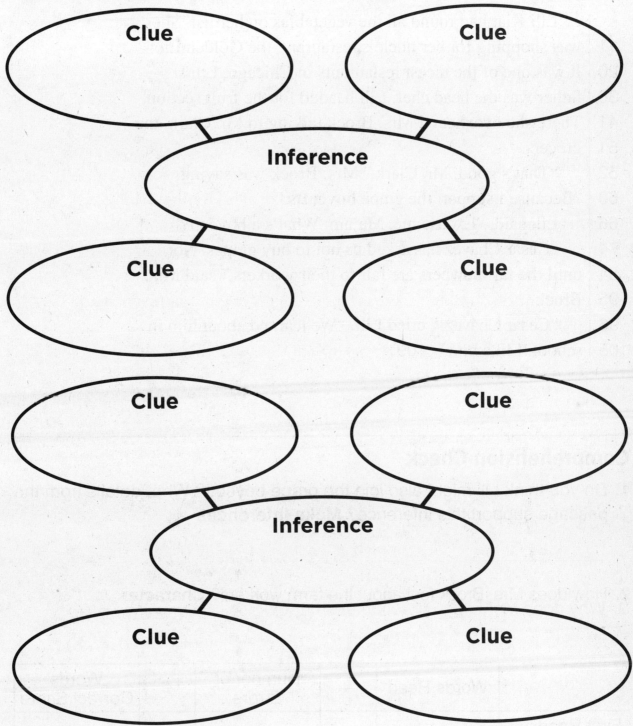

Clue

Clue

Inference

Clue

Clue

Clue

Clue

Inference

Clue

Clue

How does the information you wrote in the Inferences Word Web help you to generate questions about *My Diary from Here to There*?

 At Home: Have the student use the chart to retell the story.

© Macmillan/McGraw-Hill

As I read, I will pay attention to end punctuation in each sentence.

	Lili Kiat had found all the vegetables on her list. She
11	was shopping for her uncle's restaurant, the Golden Lion.
20	It was one of the nicest restaurants in Chicago. Lili's
30	father was the head chef. Lili headed for the fruit section.
41	There she **overheard** Mrs. Brock talking to Mr. Clark, the
51	grocer.
52	"That's good, Mr. Clark," Mrs. Brock was saying.
60	"Because I support the grape **boycotts**."
66	Lili said, "Excuse me, Ma'am. What's a boycott?"
74	"César Chávez has asked us not to buy grapes. Not
84	until the farm owners are fair to their workers," said Mrs.
95	Brock.
96	"César Chávez!" cried Lili. "We learned about him in
105	school. I like him." 109

Comprehension Check

1. Do you think Lili might also join the grape boycott? What details from the passage support this inference? **Make Inferences**

2. How does Mrs. Brock feel about the farm workers? **Character**

	Words Read	–	Number of Errors	=	Words Correct Score
First Read		–		=	
Second Read		–		=	

At Home: Help the student read the passage, paying attention to the goal at the top of the page.

Name _____

If a person writes down what he or she sees at a historic time or place, they create a **primary source.** It can be a letter, a journal, or a personal history. A primary source is written in the first person, in the writer's own words.

Read the following passage. It is part of an oral history told by a woman named Amalie Klein. She came to the United States from Russia in 1911.

Two weeks we were on the ship. . . . My dad was sick all the way through. . . one day I was dizzy. That was in the middle of the ocean and it was foggy. The whistle blew all day long and the other whistle with the ships coming and going. They whistled so they wouldn't collide, you know. It was wobbly, they had to put the tarp over the top of the ship, because the waves hit over the top. When it was nice we could see those great big fish dive in bunches in the ocean. Finally, when we got toward port we saw the seagulls coming, flying, following the ship. . . .

Then answer the questions below.

1. What was the weather like in the middle of the ocean? _____

2. How long were they on the ship? _____

3. What did Amalie see when the ship got close to port? _____

4. Who would be most interested in Amalie's story? Circle the best answer.

    a. someone trying to learn what immigrants' journeys were like

    b. someone studying seagulls

    c. no one would be interested

At Home: Help the student to interview a family member about a childhood experience.

The language a word comes from and the word or words that make it up are the **origin** of a word. A word's origin or history can help you understand its meaning. Some entries in a dictionary or glossary include a word's origin.

chop suey *noun.* a Chinese-American dish made of a mix of vegetables and small pieces of meat. *word origin:* from *shap sui,* a phrase in Cantonese that means "odds and ends".

telescope *noun.* an instrument, usually in the form of a tube, that makes distant objects look closer and larger. *word origin:* from *telescopium,* which goes back to the Greek words *tele* (far off) and *skopion* (to look or examine).

Read the entries above and then answer the questions.

1. What does *chop suey* mean? _____

_____

2. Which language does *chop suey* come from? _____

3. What does *telescope* mean? _____

_____

4. Which language does *telescope* come from? _____

5. Is the meaning of *telescope* today the same as its original meaning?

Why? _____

_____

At Home: Help the student look up 5 words in a dictionary to see if you can find their origin.

Name _____

Say the words *shed* and *wish.* You will hear the **sh** sound in each word. The letter pairs **sh**, **th**, and **ph** are unusual. In each one a consonant pairs with **h** to form a new sound.
- th   <u>th</u>irty, bo<u>th</u>er
- sh   <u>sh</u>ed, ru<u>sh</u>
- ph   <u>ph</u>one, gra<u>ph</u>

The letter pair **wh** sounds about the same as the letter **w** by itself.

wh   <u>wh</u>isk, no<u>wh</u>ere

Add *sh*, *ph*, *wh*, or *th* to the blanks below to create words.

1. _____anks

2. _____oto

3. tra_____

4. bo_____er

5. _____out

6. ten_____

7. _____ip

8. _____ink

9. fi_____

10. gra_____

11. bru_____

12. _____ese

13. no_____ere

14. _____ove

15. head_____one

16. wa_____er

At Home: Have the student find four examples each of words with the *sh*, *ph*, *wh*, or *th* sounds in books, magazines, and newspapers.

Name _____

Write a vocabulary word to replace each underlined word in the sentences below.

| temples | dynasties | heritage | preserve | overjoyed |

1. Ancient <u>places of worship</u> _____ from the Ming dynasty can still be visited in China today.

2. The palace was part of China's <u>inheritance from the past</u> _____.

3. When the excavation of the tomb was done, the scientists were <u>very</u>

   <u>happy</u> _____ that they had found some wonderful artwork.

4. The town council decided to <u>repair and save</u> _____ an unusual house on the main square.

5. The <u>powerful families</u> _____ of China had a big effect on the nation's history.

6. Write a sentence using one of the vocabulary words.

   _____

   _____

Name _____

Sometimes you must read carefully to understand exactly
what is in a text.
- A **fact** is a statement that can be proven.
- An **opinion** is a statement of someone's belief that
cannot be proven.

Chinese peasants digging a well discovered the tomb of Emperor Qin.
Built over 2,000 years ago, it contained over 7,500 life-size figures of
warriors. The figures included ordinary soldiers, archers, officers, and
even chariots with horses. All were made of terracotta clay and then baked
in a kiln. Scientists believe that they were supposed to protect the emperor
in the afterlife. If you visit the museum where they are being preserved,
you will be impressed by them, no matter what they were supposed to do.

**Read the paragraph above. Then read the following statements.
Mark each statement *F* for fact or *O* for opinion. Read the
passage again if you want.**

_____ **1.** Emperor Qin's tomb had more than 7,500 figures.

_____ **2.** The warrior figures were made of clay.

_____ **3.** You will be impressed by the figures.

_____ **4.** The warrior figures are now in a museum.

_____ **5.** Digging up the clay warriors was a waste of money.

_____ **6.** The warriors should be sent to museums around the world so that
more people can see them.

At Home: With the student, take turns making statements
and identifying them as facts or opinions.

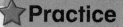
Name _____

As you read *Stealing Beauty*, fill in the Fact and Opinion Chart.

Fact	Opinion

How does the information you wrote in the Fact and Opinion Chart
help you to analyze and make inferences about *Stealing Beauty*?

 At Home: Have the student use the chart to retell the story.

© Macmillan/McGraw-Hill

As I read, I will pay attention to tempo.

	Giant pandas spend their days eating bamboo. Pandas
8	cannot digest the plant easily. So it is hard for their bodies
20	to use bamboo's nutrients. Pandas need to eat a lot of
31	bamboo in order to stay healthy.
37	Pandas have to peel off the hard outside part of the
48	bamboo to get at the softer part under it. Their wrists have
60	a long bone that they can use like a thumb. Having this
72	bone lets them grab and tear the bamboo. Then the pandas
83	crush the bamboo stems and leaves in their mouths. Panda
93	jaws are strong and their teeth are flat.
101	Pandas have to spend up to 14 hours a day eating. It
112	takes a long time to chew on the 20 to 40 pounds
122	(9 to 18 kg) of bamboo they need each day. 130

Comprehension Check

1. Is it the author's opinion that pandas eat a lot of bamboo? **Fact and Opinion**

2. What is the main idea of the second paragraph? **Main Idea and Details**

	Words Read	−	Number of Errors	=	Words Correct Score
First Read		−		=	
Second Read		−		=	

© Macmillan/McGraw-Hill

At Home: Help the student read the passage, paying attention to the goal at the top of the page.

Stealing Beauty
Grade 4/Unit 2

55

Name _____

Knowing what is in different parts of a book can save you time. By previewing a book, you can decide if it's the book you need.

- **Front Cover:** lists the book's title and author
- **Back Cover:** often describes what the book is about
- **Title Page:** shows the title and author along with the publisher of the book
- **Table of Contents:** lists the chapters and the page on which each chapter begins
- **Glossary:** a dictionary for the book, with the meanings and pronunciations for new words
- **Index:** shows the different topics in the book and the pages where you can find them

Circle the letter of the correct answer.

1. What part of a book contains a list of the book's chapters?
   a. front cover
   b. table of contents
   c. title page

2. What part of a book tells you how to pronounce a word?
   a. glossary
   b. index
   c. table of contents

3. Which **two** parts of a book tell you who wrote it?
   a. front cover
   b. title page
   c. index

4. What part of a book often has a summary of what is contained in a book?
   a. front cover
   b. back cover
   c. title page

© Macmillan/McGraw-Hill

 At Home: Have the student pick a favorite book and point out some of the parts listed above.

Name _____

- Adding **s** to most nouns makes them plural. One person has a **throat,** but in a group of people there are many **throats.**
- Nouns that end in **s, sh, ch, x,** or **z** require you to add **es.** The plural of a single **brush** is **brushes.**
- If a noun ends with a **consonant** and **y,** you must change the **y** to **i** and add **es.** One **party** becomes many **parties.**

Circle the correct plural below each word.

1. thrill

thrills   thrilles

2. bell

belles   bells

3. baby

babys   babies

4. porch

porches   porchs

5. egg

eggs   egges

6. book

bookes   books

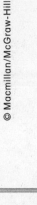 © Macmillan/McGraw-Hill

At Home: At a meal, ask the student to write down the plurals of what you're eating. For example, *apple* becomes *apples,* *tomato* becomes *tomatoes,* and *jelly* becomes *jellies.*

Name _____

shred	**thr**ob	**spr**ang	**scr**eech	**spl**ashing

All the words in the box begin with a cluster of three consonants. Say the words to yourself. Notice how the consonant sounds blend together to make a single sound.

Underline the three-consonant cluster in the following words. If there is no three-consonant cluster, draw an X through the word.

1. throat

2. graph

3. split

4. script

5. slit

6. shrink

7. screen

8. store

9. winding

10. throwing

© Macmillan/McGraw-Hill

At Home: Together, look in some of the student's books to find words that begin with the three-consonant clusters *shr, thr, spr, scr,* and *spl.*

Name _____

| hilarious | handy | nowadays | independence |
| convinced | dizzy | whirlwind | mischief |

Write each vocabulary word next to its meaning.

1. persuaded, talked into _____

2. having a spinning feeling _____

3. useful _____

4. freedom _____

5. being naughty _____

6. in the present _____

7. small windstorm _____

8. very funny _____

Write two sentences using words from the box.

9. _____

_____

_____

10. _____

_____

_____

A **problem** is a question, situation, or condition that is difficult to solve.
A **solution** is the act or method of solving the problem.
The plot of many stories involves a problem and a solution.

Read the story. Then circle the correct answer to each question.

A boy named Justin once rode his bike past a home for children. He saw that the children there didn't have bikes to ride. So he decided to get them bikes. He didn't have a lot of money to spend, so he couldn't just buy a lot of bikes. What Justin did was look for old bikes to fix up for the children. When people heard about what he was doing, they started bringing him their old bikes and donating money so that he could buy the parts he needed. Justin was then able to rebuild many more bikes and give them away.

1. What problem does Justin see?

   a. The children at the home don't have bikes.

   b. Justin can't find anyone to ride his bike with.

2. What is Justin's solution?

   a. He will give them his bike.

   b. He will fix old bikes and donate them.

3. What makes Justin's solution hard?

   a. He is really busy.

   b. He doesn't have a lot of money for parts.

4. How do people help Justin solve this problem?

   a. They help him fix up old bikes.

   b. They bring him old bikes and give him money for parts.

© Macmillan/McGraw-Hill

At Home: Ask the student to tell you about a
problem he or she has solved.

As you read *How Ben Franklin Stole the Lightning,* fill in the
Problem and Solution Chart.

Problem

↓

Action

↓

Action

↓

Action

↓

Solution

How does the information you wrote in the Problem and Solution Chart help
you to generate questions about *How Ben Franklin Stole the Lightning*?

At Home: Have the student use the chart to retell the story.

How Ben Franklin Stole the
Lightning • Grade 4/Unit 2

As I read, I will pay attention to match my tempo with the energy of the passage.

	A wounded soldier lies on the battlefield. He calls out
10	for help. The sound of gunfire is closer than before. He
21	looks up to see a woman. She gives him water. Then she
33	begins to clean his wounds. The year is 1862 and the Civil
44	War has begun. The woman is Clara Barton.
52	Clara Barton was a woman with an idea. She thought
62	that all wounded soldiers should get medical treatment.
70	She believed that a group of volunteers could be set up to
82	make sure that this happened. She wanted this group
91	to provide help for everyone; not only in times of war, but
103	whenever help was needed. She found others to help her.
113	Her work left us with a life saving idea — the American
124	Red Cross. 126

Comprehension Check

1. What problem did Clara Barton see and what did she do about it? **Problem and Solution**

2. State your opinion about Clara Barton. **Fact and Opinion**

	Words Read	–	Number of Errors	=	Words Correct Score
First Read		–		=	
Second Read		–		=	

At Home: Help the student read the passage, paying attention to the goal at the top of the page.

- **Figurative language** uses words in fresh ways to create vivid descriptions. Sometimes the words exaggerate the truth of what really happened. Sometimes one image is compared with another.
- **Alliteration** is the repetition of the same first letter or consonant sound in a series of words.

Books on babies, books on bells,

Books on boots and bicycles.

Ben believed in books to borrow,

Lending them brought new tomorrows.

Ben Franklin was a brilliant man;

He caught lightning in his hand.

He held it tight and tamed its fire;

He burned bright and still inspires.

_____

_____

1. Circle the words that show alliteration.

2. Underline the sentences that show figurative language.

3. Add two lines to the poem. Include alliteration or figurative language.

4. Can fire be tamed? What is fire being compared to?

_____

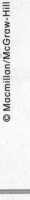

At Home: Together, write sentences that have alliteration, and sentences that have figurative language.

How Ben Franklin Stole the
Lightning • Grade 4/Unit 2

63

The meaning of an **idiom** often can't be guessed by knowing the meaning of each word. For example: "It's raining cats and dogs" has nothing to do with animals. Instead it means, "It's raining heavily." You can usually find idioms in a dictionary by looking up the most important word in the phrase.

Circle the correct answer.

1. Under which word in the dictionary would you most likely find "the apple of one's eye"?

   a. apple

   b. the

2. What does "the apple of one's eye" mean?

   a. someone whose eyes are shaped like apples

   b. someone who is well loved

3. Under which word are you most likely to find "egg on my face"?

   a. face

   b. egg

4. What does "egg on my face" mean?

   a. having scrambled eggs on your face

   b. feeling embarrassed

5. Complete this sentence:

   I sure had egg on my face after I _____

   _____

6. Complete this sentence:

   I could tell he was the apple of her eye _____

   _____

© Macmillan/McGraw-Hill

At Home: See if you and the student can think of idioms with *arm, leg, hand,* or *foot.*

Name _____

The **/är/** sound you see underlined in _argue_ and _spark_ is usually spelled _ar_.

The **/ôr/** sound underlined in _stormy_ and _fort_ is usually spelled _or_. However, it is sometimes spelled _ar_, as in the word _warp_.

Read the definition. Look at the word next to it. Decide whether the missing letter is an _a_ or an _o_. Fill in the missing letter. Then write the whole word.

1. **a.** a place where animals and crops are raised   f____rm   _____

   b. the shape of an object   f____rm   _____

2. **a.** a harbor   p____rt   _____

   b. a piece of something   p____rt   _____

3. **a.** a stiff rectangular piece of paper   c____rd   _____

   b. a thin rope made of several strands twisted together   c____rd   _____

Circle the correct sound for each word.

4. ward   5. start   6. warm
   /är/ /ôr/   /är/ /ôr/   /är/ /ôr/

7. door   8. carpet
   /är/ /ôr/   /är/ /ôr/

At Home: Look in a magazine or book for words spelled with _ar_ or _or_. Review their pronunciations with the student.

How Ben Franklin Stole the Lightning • **Grade 4/Unit 2**

65

Name _____

apologize	genuine	harmless	cardboard
slithered	ambulance	weekdays	

Write the correct word from the box next to its meaning.

1. Monday through Friday _____

2. safe, not dangerous _____

3. moved by slipping or sliding _____

4. say you're sorry _____

5. real, sincere _____

6 a special vehicle that carries the sick and wounded _____

7. thick, stiff paper _____

Write a sentence using one of the words.

_____

_____

_____

Name _____

Authors do not always directly state what is happening or how characters are feeling in a story. Sometimes you have to use clues in the story and what you know from your own experiences to help you **make inferences**.

Read the story. Then make inferences to answer the questions.

When Maggie came home from school, she smelled something delicious. Her father was cooking spaghetti and making his special sauce. This was her absolute favorite meal, and she wondered what the special occasion was. Then she looked at the table by the door. Her report card was lying there with the rest of the mail. Her father came over and gave her a big hug.

When they sat down to eat, Maggie's brother and sister held out their plates first. But their father shook his head at them and winked at Maggie. She held out her plate, and he piled it high with spaghetti and salad.

Circle the correct answer to each question.

1. What does Maggie's report card show?
   a. She made good grades.   **b.** It shows a recipe for spaghetti.

2. How does Maggie find out what her report card shows?
   a. She reads it in her bedroom.   **b.** Her father gives her a big hug.

3. Why does Maggie's father make her favorite meal?
   a. He likes spaghetti, too.   **b.** He wants to show her he's proud of her.

4. How do you think Maggie felt when her father served her before her brother and sister?
   a. She felt special.   **b.** She felt frustrated.

© Macmillan/McGraw-Hill

At Home: Have the student make inferences about family members' thoughts and feelings based on their behavior.

As you read *Dear Mr. Winston*, fill in the Inferences Word Web.

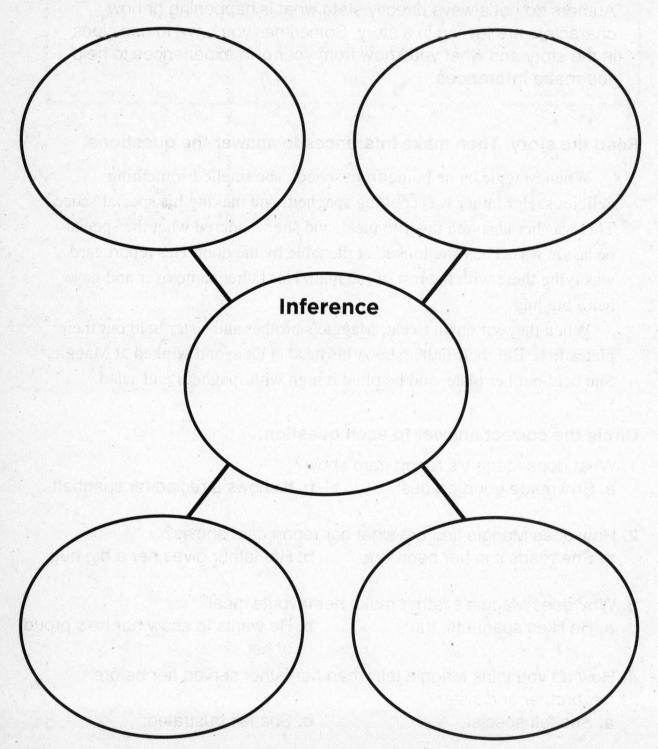

Inference

How does the information you wrote in the Inferences Word Web help you to generate questions about *Dear Mr. Winston*?

 At Home: Have the student use the chart to retell the story.

Name _____

As I read, I will pay attention to tempo.

	Snakes that live in the trees of the rain forest have a few things in
15	common. Most of these snakes are long and skinny. They also have
27	angled scales along the underside of their body. These features help the
39	snakes balance on tree branches and shrubs.
46	Snakes that live in trees have features that help them survive.
57	Some of them use camouflage. Their colors help them blend in with
69	their surroundings and hide from predators. The Amazon tree boa does
80	this by looking like a branch. But it is a genuine snake.
92	The Amazon tree boa has extra-large eyes that can spot prey. When
104	prey comes along, the snake uncoils and scoops it up. This snake stays
117	in the trees most of the time. When it spots an animal in the water, it
133	drops down and quickly swims after it. 140

Comprehension Check

1. Why might snakes that live in trees need to be long and skinny? **Make Inferences**

2. What is the main idea in the third paragraph? Name three supporting details. **Main Idea and Details**

	Words Read	−	Number of Errors	=	Words Correct Score
First Read		−		=	
Second Read		−		=	

At Home: Help the student read the passage, paying attention to the goal at the top of the page.

Dear Mr. Winston
Grade 4/Unit 2

69

© Macmillan/McGraw-Hill

Name _____

Electronic encyclopedias contain articles on many subjects. You can find information in them by using the **toolbar**. The toolbar is usually located at the top of the screen. In the toolbar, you will find items to click that will move you to different parts of the encyclopedia.

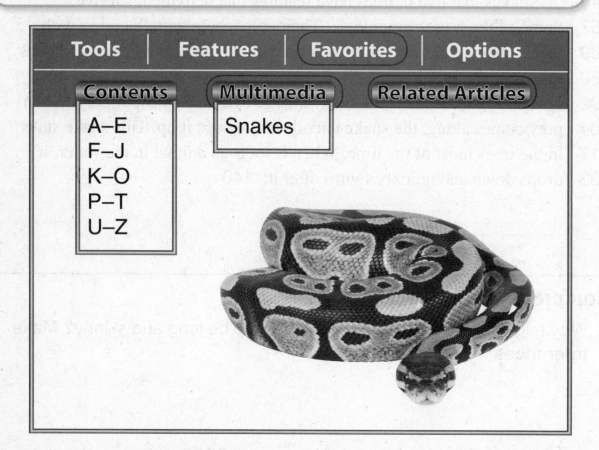

Draw lines and circles to show where you would click to find:

1. more articles about snakes

2. videos and sound clips

3. information about lizards

4. things you liked and want to see again

 At Home: Look at the sample screen above with the student. Ask him or her to explain what's shown.

The **base word** is the main part of a word. Other word parts, such as **prefixes** and **suffixes,** can be added to base words.

Prefix	Base Word	New Word
un	+ clear	= unclear
dis	+ like	= dislike

Base Word	Suffix	New Word
harm	+ less	= harmless
poison	+ ous	= poisonous

Looking for base words can help you figure out the meaning of unfamiliar words as you read.

Circle the base word in each of the following words.

1. helpful

2. enjoy

3. homeless

4. disagree

5. incorrect

6. dislike

7. restless

8. carefully

9. unlock

10. replay

 At Home: With the student, discuss how the prefixes and suffixes change the meanings of the base words above.

Some words that are spelled differently have the same sounds.
Here are some examples:
Air and spare both have the /âr/ sound.
Gear and here both have the /îr/ sound.
Identifying these sounds can help you read words correctly.

Add the letters air, are, ear, or ere to complete the following words.

1. c _____

2. fl _____

3. y _____

4. t _____

5. cl _____

6. n _____

7. d _____

8. h _____ y

9. _____ port

10. h _____

Write a short rhyming poem with an ABAB rhyme scheme, using words with /âr/ and /îr/ sounds.

_____

_____

_____

_____

At Home: Have the student make flash cards of words with
the letters *air, are, ear,* and *ere* and practice identifying the
correct pronunciation and spelling of the words.

Name _____

A. Write a word from the box to complete each sentence.

| muttered | overjoyed | overheard | convinced | flinched |

1. I wasn't supposed to know the plan, but I _____ them talking.

2. He _____ me that it was the right thing to do.

3. When she came toward me, I _____ with fear.

4. She was _____ to see us after so long.

5. He _____ about all the work he was expected to do.

B. Write the word from the box that matches each meaning.

| strikes | opportunities | harmless | independence | apologize |

6. being on your own _____

7. employees refusing to work until conditions improve

_____

8. not able to cause injury _____

9. chances to do new things _____

10. to say you're sorry _____

C. Read each statement. Write T for true if it gives the correct meaning. Write F for false if it does not.

11. An "insult" is something said or done to cause hurt feelings. ____

12. Someone who is "dizzy" is very funny. ____

13. When something "comes in handy," it is useful. ____

14. A "fluke" is the boundary between countries. ____

15. The kind of play that can hurt or annoy others is called "mischief." ____

D. Read each meaning. Then find the vocabulary word in the row of letters and circle it.

citizen	heritage	border	genuine	unions

16. the boundary between countries   s t i b o r d e r a d e

17. culture and history   f h e r i t a g e s e w

18. groups organized to protect workers' rights   a u n i o n s l v e b c

19. real   g e n u i n e x f a o r

20. a member of a country or city   v o p c i t i z e n q u

Name _____

Match each vocabulary word with its meaning by writing the number of the best answer in the blank.

interfere ____

guardian ____

awkward ____

agile ____

proclaimed ____

tottered ____

1. clumsy
2. announced
3. a person who watches over or protects
4. to concern oneself in the affairs of others without having been asked
5. able to move quickly and easily
6. wobbled

Read the paragraph. Then fill in each blank with the dark word from above that makes the most sense.

Tanesha always wanted to dance. She would watch ballerinas on television

and dream of the day when she would be like them. Finally she started

dance lessons. In the beginning, she was _____ and clumsy.

It was hard to keep her balance, and she _____ back and

forth in place. But Tanesha did not give up. She worked hard until she was

_____ and graceful as she moved across the stage.

Name _____

Usually authors write to **entertain,** to **inform,** or to **persuade.**
If the story you are reading is fiction (not true), the author's
purpose is probably to entertain. *Roadrunner's Dance* is a folk
tale. It is fiction, so the author is writing to **entertain.**
If you are reading expository nonfiction, the author's purpose is to
inform you.
If you are reading an essay and the author states an opinion and
reasons for that opinion, the author is writing to **persuade** you.

Read the following and decide on the author's purpose.

One day a robin was trying to pull a worm out of the ground in order to
eat it. "Wait," said the worm. "Let me go and I will tell you how to find a
golden treasure."

"What would I do with gold?" answered the robin, but opened his mouth
when he said this. The worm quickly tunneled his way to safety under the
ground before the robin could catch him again.

1. What type of writing is this? _____

2. What was the author's purpose in writing this? _____

Now read the following and decide on the author's purpose.

Folk tales are the best kind of stories. I like them because they have
talking animals who are clever and funny. Folk tales usually make a point
about life or explain how things started. Everyone should be reading
folk tales.

3. What type of writing is this? _____

4. What was the author's purpose in writing this?

_____

 At Home: As you read stories or articles with the student,
talk about the author's purpose for writing each one.

Name _____

As you read *Roadrunner's Dance,* fill in the Author's Purpose Map.

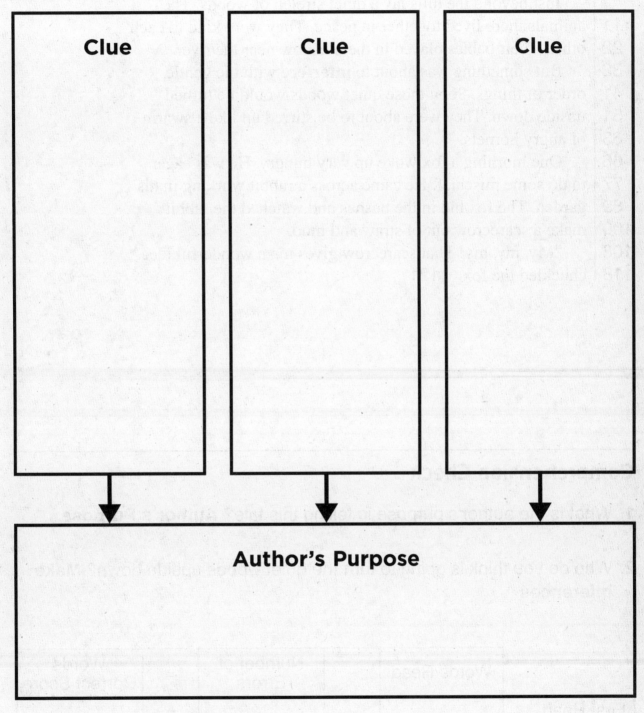

| Clue | Clue | Clue |

Author's Purpose

How does the information you wrote in the Author's Purpose Map help you to evaluate *Roadrunner's Dance*?

 At Home: Have the student use the chart to retell the story.

As I read, I will pay attention to pauses, stops, intonation, and the characters' words.

	Just beyond the hills lay a quiet stretch of woods. The
11	animals there lived together in peace. They were kind to each
22	other. Their babies played in the meadow near the river.
32	But something was about to **interfere** with the gentle
41	order of things. Soon those quiet woods would be turned
51	upside down. They were about to be stirred up like a swarm
63	of angry hornets.
66	One morning a fox woke up very hungry. He was eager
77	to do some mischief. He came across a rabbit working in his
89	garden. The fox hid in the bushes and watched the rabbit
100	make a scarecrow out of straw and mud.
108	"My, my, my! That scarecrow gives me a wonderful idea,"
118	chuckled the fox. 121

Comprehension Check

1. What is the author's purpose in telling this tale? **Author's Purpose**

2. Who do you think is going to turn the quiet woods upside down? **Make Inferences**

	Words Read	–	Number of Errors	=	Words Correct Score
First Read		–		=	
Second Read		–		=	

© Macmillan/McGraw-Hill

Roadrunner's Dance
Grade 4/Unit 3

78

At Home: Help the student read the passage, paying attention to the goal at the top of the page.

Name _____

> • **Foreshadowing** is the use of clues to hint at what is going to happen.
> • **Symbolism** is the use of an object to represent an idea.

Read the sentences below. Then on the blank line beside it, write whether it is an example of *foreshadowing* or *symbolism*.

1. With trembling fingers, Ana opened up the fortune cookie. "All will be

well if you dare to tell the truth," it said. _____

2. "Baa, baa, baa," growled the large animal approaching Lambsie. Above its brown paws, a big brown snout poked out beneath the white wool on its head, and a long brown tail swished behind. "Could you tell me the way to Farmer Fudd's farm?" the odd-looking sheep asked.

_____

3. In the hallway outside room 313, William Laughing Horse felt inside the deep pocket of his jacket to brush his fingertips against his grandfather's eagle feather. Grandpa Joe had been a great warrior. With a nod, William knocked and went in to speak with Mr. Blackwell.

_____

Now write your own examples below.

Foreshadowing: _____

_____

Symbolism: _____

_____

At Home: Brainstorm with the student to find one example of symbolism and one example of foreshadowing in movies you have seen.

A **synonym** is a word that means the same, or almost the same, as another word. For example, a synonym for **big** is **large**. A synonym for **hop** is **jump**.

Match these words from the story *Roadrunner's Dance* with their synonyms by writing one of the words from the box in each blank.

awkward	blinked	proclaimed	tottered
strange	twirling	afraid	guardian

1. protector _____

2. clumsy _____

3. scared _____

4. unusual _____

5. announced _____

6. wobbled _____

Use a thesaurus to find synonyms for two other words from *Roadrunner's Dance*. Write each word and its synonym on the short blank lines. Then on the long lines, rewrite the sentence from the story with the word replaced by the synonym.

7. _____ _____

_____

_____

8. _____ _____

_____

_____

At Home: Play a synonym game. Say a word and ask the student to say a synonym for that word. Then change roles and have the student think of a word for you.

Say these words and listen for the sound of the vowel + **r**:
twirl, hurl, person, pearl. This is the /ûr/ sound.

The /ûr/ sound has a different spelling in each word. In these four
words, /ûr/ is spelled **ir, ur, er,** and **ear.**

**Circle the vowel + r combination that makes the
/ûr/ sound in each of these words.**

1. b u r n

2. s t e r n

3. s h i r t

4. l e a r n

5. w h i r l

6. h e a r d

7. p u r p l e

8. f e r n

9. p u r s e

10. d i r t y

11. b i r t h

12. c u r l

13. c u r v e

14. p e r s o n

At Home: As the student reads, have him or her find
words that have the /ûr/ sound. Make a chart of how these
words are spelled: er, ir, ur, or ear.

Roadrunner's Dance
Grade 4/Unit 3

81

© Macmillan/McGraw-Hill

| injustice | ancestors | unfair | avoided |
| numerous | unsuspecting | segregation | |

Read each clue. Then find the vocabulary word in the row of letters and circle it.

1. Not giving someone a turn to play a game:

   i x z m n o u r t u n f a i r q p l k j y a s d f

2. Our great-great-great-great grandparents:

   r q c b a n c e s t o r s w z p o r t j k

3. Unfairness:

   s p x i n j u s t i c e m y n r t o o q e l

4. Many:

   t j x n u m e r o u s o e m y s j o p q z x g h o a r z x q o o g

5. Not aware that something is going to happen:

   r z w e a x u n s u s p e c t i n g w o

6. Keeping one race of people separate from another:

   w i j g o h u m q c p s e g r e g a t i o n w i p l j b n m x

7. Kept away from:

   w q a z s e r t a v o i d e d p y r g h u b n a d

Write three sentences using one of these vocabulary words in each.

8. _____

9. _____

10. _____

   _____

Name _____

Usually authors write to **entertain,** to **inform,** or to **persuade.**
When an author writes to inform, the sentences contain facts.
Example: Rosa Parks was arrested in 1955.
When an author writes to persuade, he or she states a certain
point of view and may give reasons for it or suggest actions the
reader should take. Example: We should treat everyone equally.

**Read the following sentences. Think about the author's purpose.
After each sentence write *inform* or *persuade.***

1. Christine and Martin were born in the same room. _____

2. The house belonged to their grandparents. _____

3. People should speak out against injustice. _____

4. Segregation was the worst period in our history. _____

5. One day the boys said that they couldn't play together anymore.

   _____

6. Shortly afterward the family sold the store and moved away.

   _____

7. It is important to treat everyone with fairness and respect.

   _____

8. Never give up hope. _____

© Macmillan/McGraw-Hill

At Home: Read sentences from the editorial pages of a newspaper
or from magazine articles with the student. Discuss which sentences
were written to inform and which were written to persuade.

My Brother Martin **83**
Grade 4/Unit 3

Name _____

As you read My Brother Martin, fill in the Author's Purpose Map.

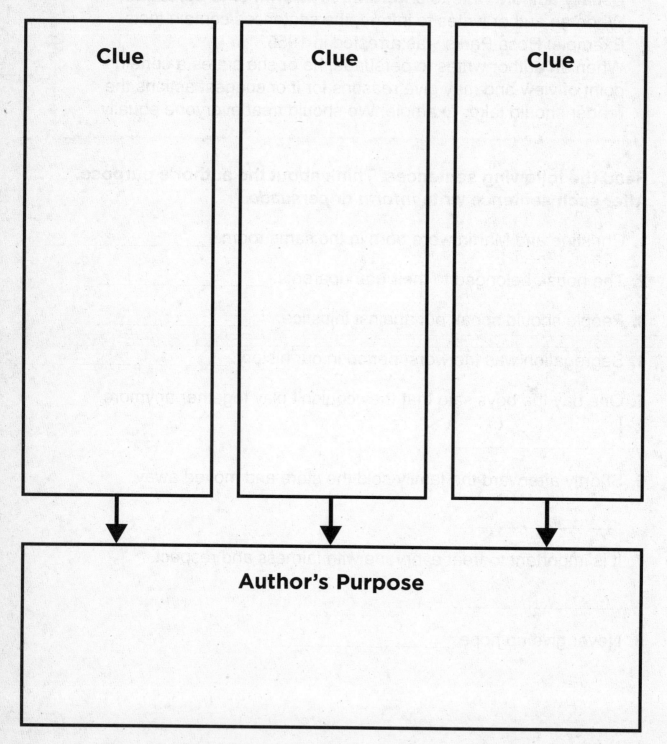

Clue	Clue	Clue

Author's Purpose

How does the information you wrote in the Author's Purpose Map help you to evaluate *My Brother Martin*?

 At Home: Have the student use the chart to retell the story.

© Macmillan/McGraw-Hill

Name _____

As I read, I will pay attention to punctuation in each sentence.

	Harriet Tubman was a small woman. She never went to
10	school. She was forced to work hard jobs as a young child.
22	She suffered blackouts from a head injury. Yet some
31	people thought she was so dangerous that they offered a
41	$40,000 reward for her capture.
46	Harriet Tubman ran away from slavery. But she never
55	ran from the chance to help others. She helped hundreds of
66	other enslaved people. She returned to the South
74	**numerous** times to free other captives.
80	When war broke out, she became a nurse. She used
90	healing tips from her ancestors to cure sick soldiers. Then
100	she became a spy for the Northern Army. After the war,
111	Harriet Tubman worked to make life less **unfair** for
120	women and poor people. 124

Comprehension Check

1. Did the author write this to entertain? If not, what is the author's purpose? **Author's Purpose**

2. What inference can you make about Harriet Tubman as a person? **Make Inferences**

	Words Read	–	Number of Errors	=	Words Correct Score
First Read		–		=	
Second Read		–		=	

At Home: Help the student read the passage, paying attention to the goal at the top of the page.

- **Letters** are written messages that people send to each other.
- A **salutation** is the line in the letter in which the writer greets the person to whom it was written. For example, "Dear Mrs. Parks."
- The **body** of the letter is the main part of the letter, containing the writer's message.

Read the lines below. On the blanks, write *salutation* or *body* to identify the different parts of a letter.

1. Dear Mrs. Lincoln: _____

2. Thank you for inviting me to your birthday party. I had a wonderful time.

_____

3. Hi, Chandra, _____

4. Dear Michael, _____

5. Please send me four jars of Miracle Glow car wax and a package of

buffing cloths. _____

On the lines below, write your own salutation and body.

Salutation: _____

Body: _____

_____

 At Home: Have the student write a letter to a friend or family member. Make sure the letter has a salutation and a body.

© Macmillan/McGraw-Hill

Name _____

> Prefixes like ***un-*** and ***re-*** can change the meaning of a word when they are placed before it.
> - ***Un-*** means "not." For example, ***unsure*** means "not sure."
> - ***Re-*** means "again." For example, ***recheck*** means "to check again."

Read each sentence. Add the prefix *re-* or *un-* to the underlined word as directed. Then define the new word.

1. Lee went to the post office to <u>send</u> a letter.

New word with *re-*: _____

New word's meaning: _____

2. Emma was <u>kind</u> to the dog.

New word with *un-*: _____

New word's meaning: _____

3. The rules were <u>fair</u>.

New word with *un-*: _____

New word's meaning: _____

4. María <u>packed</u> the box carefully.

New word with *re-*: _____

New word's meaning: _____

5. <u>Fortunately</u>, the directions from the airport to our hotel were really <u>clear</u>.

New words with *un-*: _____

_____

New words' meanings: _____

_____

© Macmillan/McGraw-Hill

 At Home: Have the student list four words that begin with each of these prefixes.

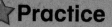
Look at these words: **kneel, climb, calm, wreck.**

In these words, one letter is silent.

- In **kneel** the silent letter is **k**.
- In **climb** the silent letter is **b**.
- In **calm** the silent letter is **l**.
- In **wreck** the silent letter is **w**.

Circle the silent letters in each of these words:

1. w r i t e   5. k n i t

2. k n e a d   6. p a l m

3. t h u m b s   7. w r o n g

4. w r e n c h   8. l a m b

Now think of four other words with the same silent letters. Write the words on the blanks and circle the silent letters in each one.

9. _____

10. _____

11. _____

12. _____

At Home: Read a story or article with the student and find as many "silent letter" words as possible. Ask your child to note which letters in each word are silent.

| identified | enterprising | persistence | venture |

Circle the letter of the correct answer in the statements below.

1. People who choose a more difficult **venture** each time they reach their goal
   a. like to sleep late.
   b. are looking for trouble.
   c. are not afraid to take chances.

2. People with **persistence**
   a. like to travel.
   b. will not give up.
   c. do not get it.

3. If someone has been **identified**
   a. he or she must give up all hope.
   b. it will cost him or her money.
   c. someone else knows who he or she is.

4. **Enterprising** people are
   a. hard-working.
   b. lazy.
   c. angry.

Draw a line to connect each vocabulary word with its synonym.

1. identified   named

2. enterprising   project

3. persistence   perseverance

4. venture   daring

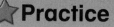
Writers often compare or contrast things when they are writing a description.

- When you **compare** two or more things, ask yourself, "How are these things alike?"
- When you read, watch for words like *both, each, like, same, also,* and *too* to signal comparisons.
- When you **contrast** two or more things, ask yourself, "How are these things different?"
- When you read, watch for words like *different, but, on the other hand,* and *however* to signal contrasts.

Read this passage.

Cucumbers are found in the grocery store in the produce department. Sea cucumbers live in the sea and are related to starfish. Some sea cucumbers look a little like those from the store. However, sea cucumbers are animals. The ones in the store are vegetables.

Write two ways that sea cucumbers and regular cucumbers are alike in the *Compare* column. Then write two ways that they are different in the *Contrast* column.

Compare (How Alike?)	Contrast (How Different?)

© Macmillan/McGraw-Hill

 At Home: Together, compare and contrast different objects in your home.

Name _____

As you read *Kid Reporters at Work,* fill in the Venn Diagram.

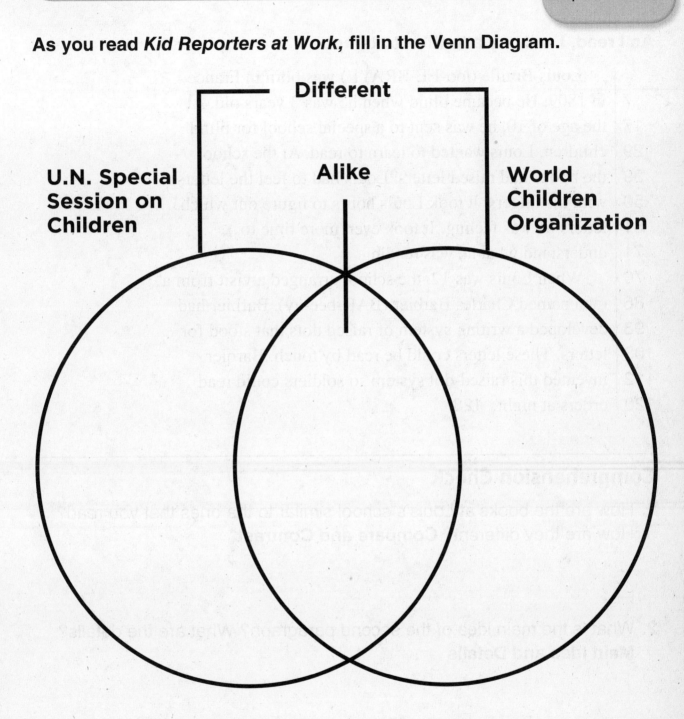

Different

**U.N. Special
Session on
Children**

Alike

**World
Children
Organization**

How does the information you wrote in the Venn diagram help you to
summarize *Kid Reporters at Work*?

At Home: Have the student use the chart to retell the story.

As I read, I will pay attention to tempo.

	Louis Braille (loo-EE-BRAYL) was born in France
7	in 1809. He became blind when he was 3 years old. At
17	the age of 10, he was sent to a special school for blind
29	children. Louis wanted to learn to read. At the school
39	the books had raised letters. Louis had to feel the letters
50	with his fingers. It took Louis hours to figure out which
61	letters he was feeling. It took even more time to
71	understand what he was reading.
76	When Louis was 12, the school arranged a visit from a
86	man named Charles Barbier (BAR-bee-ay). Barbier had
93	developed a writing system of raised dots that stood for
103	letters. These letters could be read by touch. Barbier
112	invented this raised-dot system so soldiers could read
120	orders at night. 123

Comprehension Check

1. How are the books at Louis's school similar to the ones that you read? How are they different? **Compare and Contrast**

2. What is the main idea of the second paragraph? What are the details? **Main Idea and Details**

	Words Read	–	Number of Errors	=	Words Correct Score
First Read		–		=	
Second Read		–		=	

At Home: Help the student read the passage, paying attention to the goal at the top of the page.

© Macmillan/McGraw-Hill

Name _____

You can use the **electronic card catalog** to find books in the library. There are three main ways to search the catalog:
- If you are trying to find books by a certain author, search **by author.**
- If you are looking for a book and you know the title, search **by title.**
- If you need books about a certain subject, search **by subject.**

The books you find will show up in a screen that looks something like this.

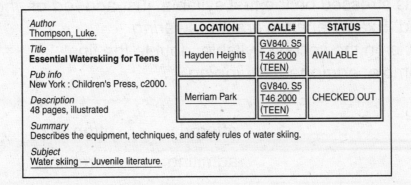

Use the electronic card entry to answer the questions below. Circle the correct answer.

1. What is the title of the book?
   a. *Thompson Luke*   **b.** *Essential Waterskiing for Teens*

2. Who is the author of the book?
   a. Hayden Heights   **b.** Luke Thompson

3. How many pages are in the book?
   a. 48   **b.** 2000

4. What is the book's status at the Merriam Park library?
   a. GV840.S5 T46 2000 (JUV)   **b.** CHECKED OUT

At Home: Have the student explain how you can search by author, title, and subject to get this book.

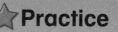
Name _____

Circle the correct spelling of each set of words.

> When a verb has one syllable + one short vowel (as in *sag, ban, dip, dot, gum*) + one consonant at the end, you double the final consonant before adding *-ed* or *-ing*: *shopped/shopping*

1. tag + ed   tagged   taged

2. drop + ing   dropping   droping

> When a two-syllable verb ends in a short vowel and a single consonant and is stressed on the first syllable, just add *-ed* or *-ing* to the base word. Example: *answered/answering*
> But if the stress is on the second syllable, double the final consonant. Example: *equipped/equipping*

3. offer + ed   offered   offerred

4. admit + ing   admiting   admitting

> If the word ends in a vowel + *y*, the base word doesn't change when you add *-ed* or *-ing*. Example: *annoyed/annoying*
> But if the verb ends in a consonant + *y*, change the *y* to *i* before adding *-ed*. Example: supply + ed = supplied

5. marry + ed   marryed   married

6. try + ed   tried   tryed

At Home: Together, find verbs in student's books, a newspaper, or a magazine that end with *-ed* and *-ing*. Ask student for the correct spelling of the base word.

When **c** and **g** are followed by **e, i,** or **y,** their sounds are soft.
- The soft **c** is pronounced like the letter **s**:
  Examples: *certain, center.*
- The soft **g** is pronounced like the letter **j**:
  Examples: *village, ginger.*

Circle each soft c or g in the following words.

1. citizen

2. fragile

3. cage

4. gymnasium

5. license

6. cycle

7. Explain the pronunciation of the *c* and *g* in *cage.*

_____

_____

_____

8. Explain the pronunciation of the 2 *cs* in *cycle.*

_____

_____

_____

At Home: Together, find examples of soft *c* and soft *g* in the
student's books or in newspapers and magazines.

Kid Reporters at Work
Grade 4/Unit 3

95

Name _____

patchwork	mysterious	responsibility	midst
loosened	amazement	sores	

Write each vocabulary word next to its definition.

1. in the middle	_____
2. scraps of cloth sewn together	_____
3. painful spots on the body	_____
4. made something less tight	_____
5. hard to explain or understand	_____
6. having to take care of something	_____
7. a feeling of being very surprised	_____

Write a sentence using one of the vocabulary words.

8. _____

_____

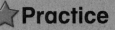
> Events happen in a certain order, or **sequence.** Learning to see the sequence of events helps you make sense of what you read.

Read the passage below. Then circle the correct answer for the questions that follow.

Mary wanted to enter the science essay contest. She decided to write her essay on monarch butterflies. Mary searched websites on the Internet. She also read books and magazine articles on monarch butterflies.

Mary took careful notes and made an outline. She then wrote her essay and typed the final draft. Mary proudly handed in the essay to her science teacher. One month later, Mary found out that her essay won first prize.

1. What did Mary do first?

   a. Mary wrote an outline for her essay.

   b. Mary gave her essay to her teacher.

   c. Mary decided to learn about monarch butterflies.

2. What did Mary do before she wrote her essay?

   a. Mary put all of her scraps of information in a box.

   b. Mary found out that her essay won first prize.

   c. Mary took careful notes and made an outline.

3. What happened last?

   a. Mary read about monarch butterflies.

   b. Mary found out that her essay won first prize.

   c. Mary typed the final draft of her essay.

 At Home: Read the passage with the student. Talk about how your child chose each answer.

As you read _Mystic Horse_, fill in the Sequence Chart.

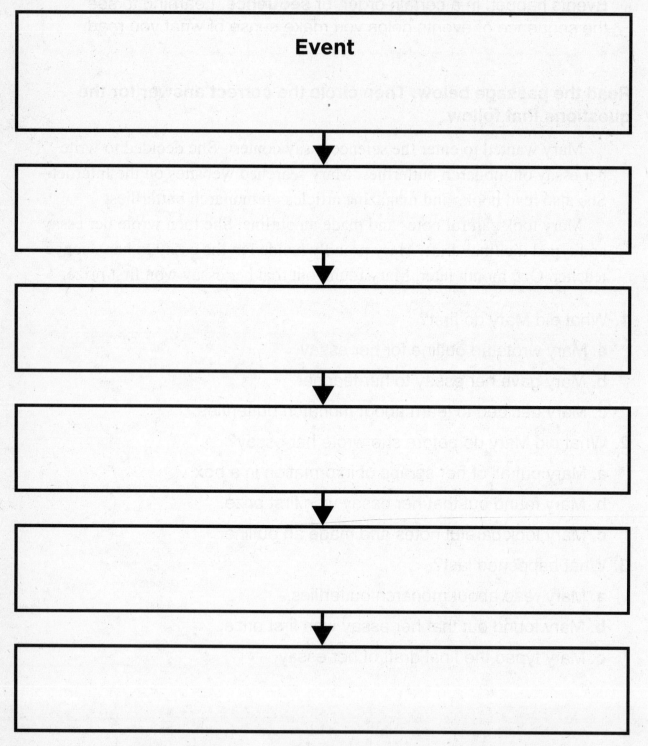

Event

How does the information you wrote in the Sequence Chart help you
to summarize _Mystic Horse_?

 At Home: Have the student use the chart to retell the story.

Name _____

As I read, I will pay attention to tempo and matching the energy and enthusiasm of every passage.

	The mother bear led her cubs through the forest. Every
10	so often she looked back to check on them. Sometimes she
21	sniffed the air. The cubs played among the leaves as they
32	followed her. A bird soared over the cubs and they looked up
44	at it.
46	When they arrived at the river, the cubs jumped in. "Be
57	careful," the mother bear said. Now it was time for the lesson.
69	The mother bear's paw went quickly in and out of the water.
81	The cubs stared in amazement at the plump, pink fish in her
93	paw. How did she do it? After a few clumsy tries, they finally
106	caught their own fish.
110	Next it was time to go to the lake. The light shining
122	through the trees made a patchwork pattern on the ground. It
133	was harder for the mother bear to see her cubs. Soon it was
146	time to go home.
150	Inside the den the mother bear and the cubs snuggled
160	together as they slept. 164

Comprehension Check

1. What did the cubs do that day? **Sequence**

2. What is the author's purpose? **Author's Purpose**

	Words Read	−	Number of Errors	=	Words Correct Score
First Read		−		=	
Second Read		−		=	

At Home: Help the student read the passage, paying attention to the goal at the top of the page.

Mystic Horse
Book 4/Unit 3

Name _____

> Websites such as online encyclopedias include articles on many subjects. They may also include underlined **links** to other articles. Articles may be split into several pages. You can click the "Next" link to move to the next page.

Read the online encyclopedia article about powwows. Then answer the questions that follow.

World Net Encyclopedia

Powwows Today

Many people think that Native American powwows don't happen today. Actually, these special gatherings take place all across America, all through the year.

Today, a powwow is a time for Native American people to gather. There are <u>dance competitions</u>. People sell crafts. There is food and games. Other people come to watch and learn.

Would you like to go to one? There could be a powwow happening near you. Just click the link below:

<u>Powwow schedule</u>

<u>Next</u>

1. What is the name of the article? _____

2. What is the article about? _____

3. What is the name of the link in the second paragraph?

_____

4. What will happen if you click **Next** at the bottom of the page? _____

_____

 At Home: Together with the student, look at an online encyclopedia homepage or news website.

© Macmillan/McGraw-Hill

Name _____

> **Homophones** are pairs of words that are pronounced the same but have different spellings and meanings. Memorizing the correct spelling and meaning of each word can help you make sense of what you read.

Homophone Examples

The *sores* on my legs kept itching until I covered them with ointment.

A hawk *soars* on air currents, seldom flapping its wings.

I saddled my *horse* and rode down to the river.

Steven was *hoarse* after talking on the phone for over an hour.

Match each homophone with its meaning by writing its number in the correct blank.

1. sores   _____ animal used for transportation

2. horse   _____ painful spots

3. soars   _____ rough-sounding voice

4. hoarse   _____ flies very high

© Macmillan/McGraw-Hill

At Home: Together with the student, talk about the meaning of another pair of homophones.

Name _____

A word that is plural describes more than one of a thing. You can form plurals in the following ways:
- To change most words to a plural, add **-s**.
- To change a word ending in **s** to a plural, add **-es**.
- If a word ends in **y**, change the **y** to **i** and add **-es**.

Complete the word equations to write the plural form of each word.

1. moss + es = _____

2. baby – y + ies = _____

3. sale + s = _____

4. belly – y + ies = _____

5. clam + s = _____

6. dress + es = _____

7. dance + s = _____

8. class + es = _____

9. activity – y + ies = _____

10. mess + es = _____

 At Home: Together with the student, look through books, magazines, or newspapers. Have the student choose five words and write them in their plural forms.

Read each clue. Then write the correct word from the box.

| technique | foolishness | inspire | evaporate |
| microscope | magnify | negatives | blizzard |

1. something scientists use to look at very small things _____

2. a very heavy snowstorm _____

3. a way of doing something _____

4. to make something look bigger _____

5. silliness _____

6. to encourage someone _____

7. films that show dark areas as light and light areas as dark

_____

8. to change from water into vapor _____

Now choose four of the words and use each in a sentence below.

9. _____

_____

10. _____

_____

11. _____

_____

12. _____

_____

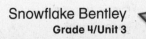

When you **summarize,** you tell the most important parts of what you have read. You should include the main idea and the most important details in your summary. Don't get caught up in trying to explain every little aspect of what you read about.

Read the selection. Circle the letter beside the best response to each question.

Many people still remember the "Storm of the Century," from the winter of 1993. It was one of the biggest ever to hit the country. It formed in the Gulf of Mexico, then traveled across the Florida panhandle and all the way up to Maine. It left more snow over a greater area than any other storm had. Alabama got a foot of snow. New York got more than three feet. High winds caused drifts of snow up to 20 feet high. Half of the people in the country were affected by the storm. Flights were canceled and roads were closed. Many people lost power. In some places, snow fell at the rate of two to three inches per hour.

1. Which is the main idea?
   a. The "Storm of the Century" had high winds.
   b. The "Storm of the Century" was one of the biggest to hit the United States.

2. Which detail is more important?
   a. It traveled from Florida up to Maine.
   b. It traveled across the Florida panhandle.

3. Which detail is more important?
   a. Half of the people in the country were affected by it.
   b. Some flights were canceled.

4. Which is the better way to summarize the paragraph?
   a. In a big snowstorm, snow falls quickly
   b. The "Storm of the Century" left large amounts of snow from Alabama to Maine. Many people were affected by it.

At Home: Tell the student about your memories of a big storm. Have him or her summarize your story.

Name _____

As you read *Snowflake Bentley*, fill in the Main Idea Web.

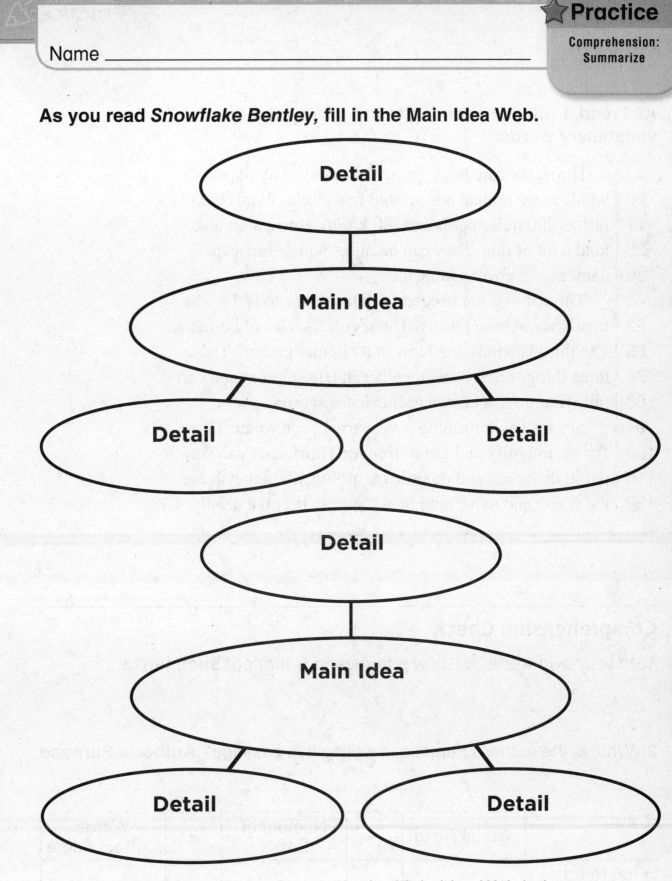

How does the information you wrote in the Main Idea Web help you evaluate *Snowflake Bentley*?

 At Home: Have the student use the chart to retell the story.

As I read, I will pay attention to the pronunciation of vocabulary words.

	Hurricanes are huge, powerful storms. High-speed
6	winds move around and around in a circle. Winds travel as
17	fast as 200 miles per hour (300 km/h). Hurricanes also
25	hold a lot of rain. They can be miles wide. Hurricane
36	damage can cover a large area.
42	Three things are needed for a hurricane to form. The
52	first is warm ocean water. The second is a lot of humid air.
65	The third is winds that blow in a circular pattern. These
76	three things often come together in late summer and early
86	fall. That time is known as hurricane season.
94	Storms begin forming over warm ocean water. These
102	storms **magnify** and grow stronger. Hurricanes can stay
110	out in the ocean and do little harm. But when they leave
122	the ocean and move onto land they can become deadly. 132

Comprehension Check

1. In your own words, tell how a hurricane is formed. **Summarize**

2. What is the author's purpose in writing this passage? **Author's Purpose**

	Words Read	–	Number of Errors	=	Words Correct Score
First Read		–		=	
Second Read		–		=	

At Home: Help the student read the passage, paying attention to the goal at the top of the page.

> **Imagery** is the use of vivid words and descriptions to create a picture in the reader's mind.
> **Figurative language** is a form of expression that uses language creatively. Similes and metaphors are examples of figurative language.

Read the haikus below and think about how they use imagery and figurative language. Then circle the letter of the correct answer to each question.

1. The driest desert
   Is paradise after rain
   Comes to create change.

   What is the desert compared to?
   a. paradise   **b.** rain

2. Thunderstorm arrives.
   Lightning illumines the sky.
   Night becomes bright day.

   How does lightning change night?
   a. It is not quiet.   **b.** It becomes like day.

3. Fog in the morning
   Makes of our quiet village
   A planet unknown.

   How does fog affect the neighborhood?
   a. Fog changes it into a mysterious place.
   b. Fog sends it through space.

4. The storm is over.
   The sun, like a waking dream,
   Streams through darkest clouds.

   What two things are being compared?
   a. the sun and a dream   **b.** the storm and clouds

At Home: Have the student choose a favorite toy or article of clothing and use figurative language to compare it to something else.

Snowflake Bentley
Grade4/Unit 3

107

© Macmillan/McGraw-Hill

Name _____

Sometimes a dictionary will give you different **meanings** for
one word.

drop *noun* **1.** a small, round amount of liquid. *A drop of rain fell
on my head.* **2.** a decline in the amount of something. *There was a*
drop *in the number of kids in my class when the flu hit.*
verb **1.** to fall in drops. *Thunder rolled, and the rain began to*
drop. **2.** to make something fall. *I dropped my pack on the floor.*

The noun *drop* has two meanings. The verb *drop* has two
meanings.

**Use the dictionary entry above to answer the two questions
that follow each sentence.**

He dropped all of the boxes when the rain started.

1. Is *dropped* used as a noun or a verb in the sentence above?

_____

2. Which dictionary meaning of *dropped* is used?

_____

I only felt one drop of rain.

3. Is *drop* a noun or a verb in the sentence above? _____

4. Which dictionary meaning of *drop* is used?

_____

Oil dropped from the hole in the pipe.

5. Is *dropped* used as a noun or a verb in the sentence above?

_____

6. Which dictionary meaning of *dropped* is used?

_____

© Macmillan/McGraw-Hill

At Home: Use a dictionary, book, or magazine to find other
multiple-meaning words. Discuss their different meanings.

Name _____

When two smaller words are put together to make one larger word, the new word is called a **compound word**.
The small words can help you figure out how to say the compound word and what it means.
backyard = back + yard = a yard in back of a house

Write the two smaller words that form each compound word. Then write the meaning of the compound word.

1. raindrop _____ + _____

Meaning: _____

2. snowflake _____ + _____

Meaning: _____

3. southeast _____ + _____

Meaning: _____

Match a word from the box with the words below to create compound words. Then write a sentence using the new word.

pour	storm	set

4. sun _____

_____

5. thunder _____

_____

At Home: Walk around your home to find compound words, like *doorknob* or *windowpane*. Ask the student to name and spell the two words that have been put together.

Snowflake Bentley
Grade4/Unit 3

109

© Macmillan/McGraw-Hill

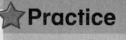
Name _____

A. Answer each question with a word from the box.

blizzard	numerous	magnify	enterprising	avoided

1. If you walked across the street so that you wouldn't have to talk to someone, what did you do? _____

2. What would you call a storm that brings a lot of snow?

    _____

3. If you make something look much bigger, what are you doing to it?

    _____

4. What is another word for "many"? _____

5. How would you describe a friend who started his own business?

    _____

B. Finish the sentences with words from the box.

responsibility	interfere	microscope
segregation	identified	

6. It's sometimes OK to _____ if you think you can help.

7. _____ in schools was once legal.

8. I _____ the problem and tried to solve it.

9. It is our _____ to return library books.

10. It looked much larger under the _____.

Name _____

C. Choose a synonym for each word from the list of vocabulary words.

| numerous | foolishness | inspire | awkward | amazement |

11. clumsy   _____

12. many   _____

13. surprise   _____

14. motivate   _____

15. silliness   _____

D. Draw a line from the vocabulary word to its meaning.

16. proclaimed   **a.** in the middle of

17. magnify   **b.** wounds

18. injustice   **c.** wrongdoing

19. sores   **d.** to make bigger

20. midst   **e.** announced in public

| risks | desperate | obedience | appreciated |
| bluffing | neglected | endured | misunderstood |

Draw lines to match each vocabulary word with its meaning.

1. almost without hope

a. risks

2. ignored

b. desperate

3. did not understand

c. obedience

4. dangers

d. appreciated

5. following orders

e. bluffing

6. was grateful

f. neglected

7. pretending to have something

g. endured

8. suffered through

h. misunderstood

Sometimes you have to **draw a conclusion** to understand what is happening in a story. To draw a conclusion, read what the text says and think about what you already know.

Tarsha let out a big yawn. She could barely keep her eyes open.

The writer doesn't come out and say, "Tarsha is tired." But you can draw that conclusion on your own.

Read the passage and answer the questions.

Brittany had wanted a dog for as long as she could remember. One day, her parents finally said yes. Her mom took her to the animal shelter, and they walked down a long row of cages until Brittany made her decision. In the very last cage sat a black dog with long ears. It did not bark or whine. It stared at Brittany with soft, dark eyes like shining stars. Brittany smiled.

1. How do you know that Brittany had never had a dog before?

_____

2. What happened at the end of the passage?

_____

3. How do you know Brittany didn't choose the first dog she saw?

_____

4. How do you think Brittany felt?

_____

At Home: Read a story with the student. Then have him or her draw a conclusion about something that the story does not tell outright.

Dear Mrs. LaRue
Grade 4/Unit 4

As you read *Dear Mrs. LaRue*, fill in the Conclusions Chart.

Text Clues	Conclusions

How does completing the Conclusions Chart help you to generate
questions about *Dear Mrs. LaRue*?

Dear Mrs. LaRue
Grade 4/Unit 4

114

At Home: Have the student use the chart to retell the story.

© Macmillan/McGraw-Hill

As I read, I will pay attention to punctuation.

	It takes a lot of work to be a movie dog. Mixed breeds
13	and purebreds alike must be well behaved. They must
22	know basic **obedience** commands like "sit down," "stay,"
30	and "come." They must also learn to perform difficult
39	tricks.
40	During the filming of a movie, a dog actor must follow
51	its trainer's commands quickly and properly. Sometimes
58	trainers aren't able to give a vocal command. So they
68	use simple hand signals instead. Sometimes fancy signals
76	are **misunderstood** by a dog actor.
82	Dog performers also must feel at ease on the movie set.
93	It's a place with many people, lots of noise, and bright
104	lights. Even with all these things going on, a dog actor
115	needs to stay focused on its trainer at all times. 125

Comprehension Check

1. Why do movie dogs need to know basic obedience commands? **Draw Conclusions**

2. Why does the author want you to know about movie dogs? **Author's Purpose**

	Words Read	–	Number of Errors	=	Words Correct Score
First Read		–		=	
Second Read		–		=	

At Home: Help the student read the passage, paying attention to the goal at the top of the page.

Dear Mrs. LaRue
Grade 4/Unit 4

115

Name _____

A **line graph** is a clear way to see some kinds of information.
Line graphs usually show changes over time.
- The **title** at the top tells what the graph is about.
- The **time information** usually runs along the bottom.
- The **quantity** usually runs up the left side of the line graph.

Mario took a survey to find out how many of his classmates had new pets each month and made a line graph to show the results.

Look at the line graph. Then answer the questions.

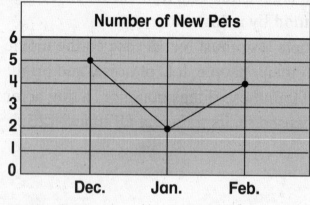

1. What is the title of this line graph?

   a. Number of New Pets

   b. Dec. Jan. Feb.

2. How many new pets were there in December?

   a. 2

   b. 5

3. How many new pets were there in February?

   a. 2

   b. 4

4. Were there more new pets in January or in February?

   a. January

   b. February

5. In which month were there the most new pets?

   a. December

   b. January

Dear Mrs. LaRue
Grade 4/Unit 4

At Home: Have the student copy the chart on a separate piece of paper, adding new pets for March and April.

Name _____

> Prefixes are **word parts**. They can be attached to the front of words to change the words' meanings. Every prefix has its own meaning.
>
> The prefix *mis-* means "badly" or "in a wrong way." For example, if you put *mis-* in front of *understood,* you get the word *misunderstood.* This means "understood in a wrong way."

Read each word in the box below. Then write each word next to its correct meaning.

misread	misbehave	mistrust
misspell	misuse	

1. spell incorrectly _____

2. use in a wrong way _____

3. read incorrectly _____

4. behave in the wrong way _____

5. not really trust _____

Write sentences using three of the words.

6. _____

7. _____

8. _____

At Home: With the student, discuss other prefixes, like *re-* and *anti-,* and how they change the meanings of words.

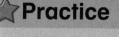
The endings *-ed* and *-ing* can be added to many words. But sometimes you have to add or drop a letter before you add the ending.

- Add a letter if the word has a **short** vowel sound and ends in a consonant, like *rip*. Double the last letter before adding *-ed* or *-ing.*

  rip + ing = rip**p**ing   rip + ed = rip**p**ed

- Drop a letter if the word ends in e. Just drop the **e** before adding the ending.

  sav**e** + ed = saved   sav**e** + ing = saving

Follow the rules above to complete these word equations.

1. have + ing = _____

2. skip + ed = _____

3. hug + ing = _____

4. taste + ing = _____

5. slam + ed = _____

6. chase + ed = _____

7. clap + ed = _____

8. write + ing = _____

9. score + ed = _____

10. sit + ing = _____

© Macmillan/McGraw-Hill

At Home: Read a story with the student, and have him or her find *-ed* and *-ing* words. Then ask him or her to identify the correct spelling of each base word.

Name _____

fade   cautiously   crisscrossed   wisdom
jealousy   disguised   faint

Read each clue. Then find the vocabulary word in the row of letters and circle it.

1. barely there   o a e w f a i n t p o i j e w r w l a

2. good sense   j u w i s d o m w a p o e a s l m d k

3. wanting what someone else has   p x c z b a n d j e a l o u s y e r

4. dressed in a costume   k o r d i s g u i s e d m a s e c j

5. marked by lines   i y r c r i s s c r o s s e d l a s e h m

6. grow dimmer   d s a l k j f a d e n m c z x w q

7. carefully   z l k a c a u t i o u s l y s n a s

8. **Write a sentence that includes at least one vocabulary word.**

_____

_____

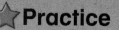
Sometimes you have to **draw conclusions** to understand what is happening in a story. To draw a conclusion, read what the text says and think about what you already know.

Damon shivered. He pulled his coat tight around his body.

The writer doesn't say, "Damon was cold." But by reading the description and using what you know about how people act when they're cold, you can draw that conclusion.

Read each sentence. Answer the questions that follow.

1. Capuchin monkeys help people who are disabled. The monkeys can be trained to do many things. They can comb their owners' hair, turn on lights, and even clean the house.
   What conclusion can you draw about Capuchin monkeys?

   _____

2. Young Capuchin monkeys are raised by families. The families adopt them and raise them almost like family members. The monkeys become friendly and happy.
   How do the families treat the monkeys?

   _____

3. When the monkey is older, it goes to a training center. The trainers give the monkeys rewards for good behavior. Then the monkey is sent to someone who needs its help.
   How do you know that the monkeys are not trained by being punished for mistakes?

   _____

4. The monkeys often become friends with their owners. Many disabled people spend hours alone each day. Their family members cannot stay home with them.
   Why do many monkeys become close friends with the disabled people they are helping?

   _____

 At Home: Read a story with the student. Ask what kind of person the main character is, and have the student provide evidence in the story to support his or her conclusion.

Name _____

As you read *The Blind Hunter*, fill in the Conclusions Chart.

Text Clues	Conclusions

How does completing the Conclusions Chart help you to generate
questions about *The Blind Hunter*?

 At Home: Have the student use the chart to retell the story.

The Blind Hunter
Grade 4/Unit 4

 121

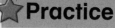
As I read, I will pay attention to pauses, stops, and intonation.

	The scene is an army hospital during World War II. A
11	wounded soldier has lost a lot of blood. The doctor says
22	that the soldier must have a blood transfusion if he is to
34	survive.
35	A nurse brings in a pint bag of blood plasma. The bag
47	is hung above the soldier's bed. A needle attached to a
59	tube enters the man's arm. The blood flows into his body.
70	The pint of plasma is soon emptied, and a nurse
80	replaces it with another. The new blood restores the
89	soldier's strength. Soon he is out of danger.
97	Years before, that same soldier would have had a
106	**faint** chance of getting the needed plasma. It wasn't
115	available at that time. 119

Comprehension Check

1. What makes you think that someone discovered a way to make plasma available? **Draw Conclusions**

2. What are the steps for giving a plasma transfusion? **Sequence**

	Words Read	–	Number of Errors	=	Words Correct Score
First Read		–		=	
Second Read		–		=	

© Macmillan/McGraw-Hill

 At Home: Help the student read the passage, paying attention to the goal at the top of the page.

Name _____

A **glossary**, which is like a small dictionary at the back of a book, can tell you
- the word's meaning, as it is used in the book;
- how to say the word correctly;
- what part of speech the word is (noun, verb, and so on).

Use the part of a glossary shown below to answer the questions.

braille   A system of printing for blind people. The letters of the alphabet in *braille* are formed by raised dots. *Blind people read* braille *by touching the dots with their fingers*.
     braille (brāl) *noun*

brilliant   1. Very bright; sparkling. 2. Very fine; splendid. *The fielder made a* brilliant *catch*. 3. Very intelligent. *He is a* brilliant *scientist*.
     bril•liant (bril′yănt) *adjective*

bureau   1. A chest of drawers. *I keep my sweaters in my* bureau. 2. A department of a government: the weather *bureau*. 3. An office or agency: a travel *bureau*.
     bu•reau (byu̇r′ ō) *noun, plural* **bureaus**.

1. Why does *brilliant* come before *bureau*?

_____

2. How many syllables does the word *brilliant* have?____

3. Which word has only one meaning?_____

4. Which word completes this sentence: *The stars look* _____.

5. What is the plural form of *bureau?*_____

At Home: With the help of a dictionary, have the student make a four-word glossary for a favorite storybook to help younger readers enjoy the book.

The Blind Hunter
Grade 4/Unit 4

Name _____

Word families are groups of words that all share a word **root** or other **part**. For example, *forward*, *backward,* and *downward* are a family based on the word part *-ward.*

You can use what you know about one word part to find out the meanings of other words. For example, *forward, backward,* and *downward* all describe directions. So if you read the word *outward,* you can figure out that it describes something that goes in an "out" direction.

The following words all belong to the same word family. Circle the part that is the same in each word.

1. wisdom   freedom   kingdom   dukedom

Knowing the meaning of shared word parts can help you read new words.

In the first two words you circled above, *-dom* means "being a certain way."

Write a word from the list for each definition:

2. being free _____

3. being wise _____

In the other two words above, -dom means "land ruled by."

Write the word that means:

4. land ruled by a king _____

5. land ruled by a duke _____

© Macmillan/McGraw-Hill

At Home: Pick one of the words above. With the student, discuss other words related to the word you chose.

Name _____

The words **happy** and **carry** end in a consonant followed by the letter **y**. When words end this way, you must do two things to add endings such as **-er** or **-ed**.

1. change the **y** to **i**   happ**i**   carr**i**
2. add the ending   happ**ier**   carr**ied**

In **carried**, the letters **ie** stand for a long **e** sound. In **happier** the letter **i** stands for the long **e** and the **-er** forms a new syllable.

Circle the _y_ in each word below. Then change the _y_ to _i_ and add the given ending. If the change added a syllable, check the box.

Words	Endings	New Words	
1. shiny	+ est	_____	☐
2. pretty	+ er	_____	☐
3. angry	+ est	_____	☐
4. sunny	+ er	_____	☐
5. bury	+ ed	_____	☐
6. hurry	+ ed	_____	☐
7. funny	+ est	_____	☐
8. ugly	+ er	_____	☐

© Macmillan/McGraw-Hill

At Home: Say a word that ends in a consonant + y. Have the student change it to a different form by changing y to i and adding -er, -ed, or -est.

The Blind Hunter
Grade 4/Unit 4

125

Name _____

Read each sentence. Fill in the sentence with the correct word from the box. Use the pictures to help you.

electrical	fuels	decayed	globe

1. During social studies, we use the large _____ to find different countries.

2. Gasoline is one of the _____ that we use every day.

3. Every room in our apartment has at least three

_____ outlets into which we can plug lamps and other things.

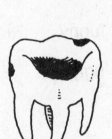

4. My dentist keeps a model of a partially

_____ tooth to show us what happens if we don't brush and floss every day.

Persuasion is how you get other people to agree with you.
You might want someone to share an opinion you have.
Or you may want them to do something.

Here are some ways that writers try to persuade their readers:

- tell the reasons for an opinion. *I like dogs because they're really smart.*
- give facts or examples that support an opinion. *Dogs can be trained to rescue people and serve as guides to the blind.*
- use words and phrases to make readers feel instead of think. *Dogs are loyal and loving. You can always count on a dog.*

Read the paragraph. Then circle the correct answers to the questions that follow.

   I believe that the city should not allow cars downtown. The traffic is really bad there. Streets are always full. People can hardly get around. We've had 30 more accidents this year than we did last year. Everyone should leave their cars when they come downtown. Downtown should be for pedestrians. Please join me! Send the mayor a letter. Let's tell her to ban automobiles downtown!

1. What is the writer persuading the reader to do?

   a. build more parking lots downtown

   b. send a letter to the mayor

   c. walk to work

2. What is one reason the writer gives for his opinion?

   a. traffic is really bad downtown

   b. the mayor doesn't know about the problem

   c. cars are better in the neighborhoods than downtown

© Macmillan/McGraw-Hill

At Home: Discuss the passage above with the student.
Does the author do a good job of persuading?

The Power of Oil
Grade 4/Unit 4

127

As you read *The Power of Oil*, fill in the Inference/Opinion Web.

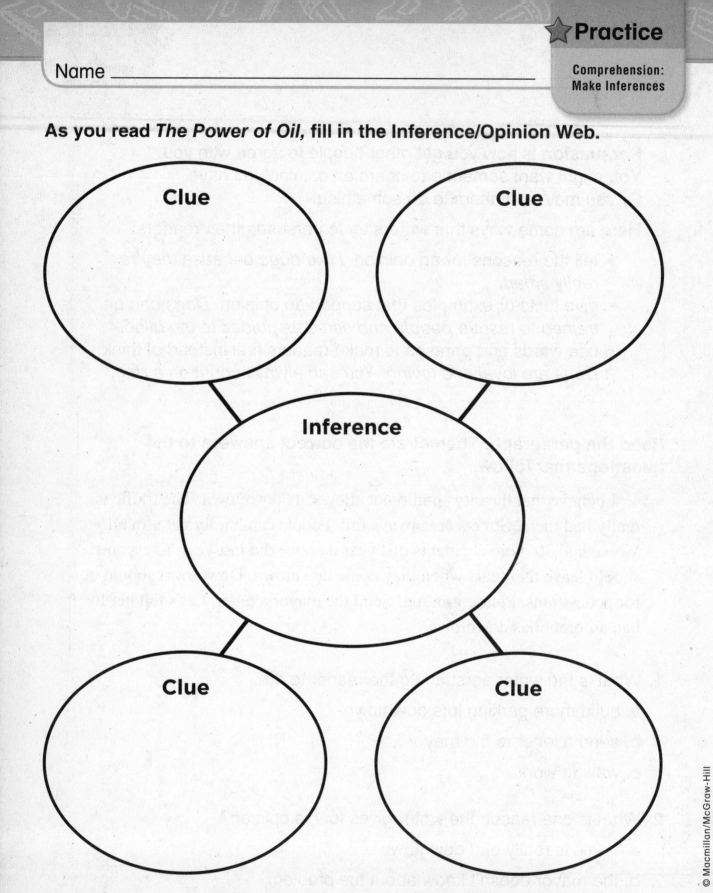

Clue

Clue

Inference

Clue

Clue

How does the information you wrote in the Inference/Opinion Web
help you generate questions about *The Power of Oil*?

 At Home: Have the student use the chart to retell the story.

© Macmillan/McGraw-Hill

As I read, I will pay attention to my pronunciation of vocabulary words and other difficult words.

	Energy is the ability to do work. There are two forms
11	of energy. The first form is kinetic energy. We call this
22	working energy. Working energy is used to throw a ball,
32	heat the stove, and run all the **electrical** things in your
43	home. The second form is potential energy. This can be
53	called stored energy. A battery contains stored energy. So
62	does food until you eat it.
68	Stored energy can be turned into working energy when
77	it is needed. When you eat, energy in food provides stored
88	energy for your body. This stored energy changes to
97	working energy so you can move. When you use a battery
108	in a toy, the stored energy turns into working energy to
119	make the toy run. 123

Comprehension Check

1. Why did the author write this passage about energy? **Author's Purpose**

2. How are kinetic energy and potential energy alike? How are they different? **Compare and Contrast**

	Words Read	–	Number of Errors	=	Words Correct Score
First Read		–		=	
Second Read		–		=	

© Macmillan/McGraw-Hill

At Home: Help the students read the passage, paying attention to the goal at the top of the pasage.

The Power of Oil
Grade 4/Unit 4

129

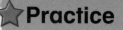

Name _____

Search engines can help you find information on the **Internet**. Type one or more **keywords** into the search engine. These are words that describe the topic that interests you.

Once you've typed in your keywords, click *Search.* The search results will bring up a list of Web pages that have the keywords you entered. Your keywords will be shown in bold. Click a page name to look at the page.

Look at the page of search results below. Then circle the correct answer for each question that follows.

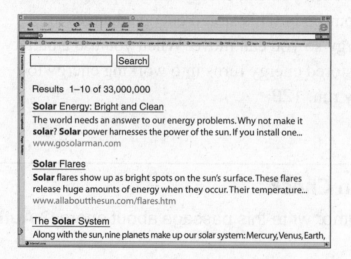

1. How many total results did the search return?

   a. 10   **b.** 33,000,000

2. What was the search keyword that brought up these results?

   a. solar   **b.** flares

3. What's another keyword you could use to find more information about solar power?

   a. energy   **b.** planets

4. What would happen if you clicked on the *Solar Flares* link?

   a. It would bring up the Web page on solar flares.   **b.** It would start another search.

At Home: Pick a topic with the student. Then think of the keywords you could use to search the Internet for information on that topic.

When you read, you will often find a word that you do not know. Sometimes other words and sentences in the text can give you **context clues** to help you figure out its meaning. You may even find a few words or a sentence that give you a **definition** of the word.

The birds <u>twittered</u>, making high chirping noises as they hopped along the branch.

Here the description of "high chirping noises" gives you a context clue that defines the meaning of *twittered*.

Read each sentence. Circle the context clues in the sentence that help you define each underlined word.

1. Some of our energy comes from <u>hydropower</u>. Water flows through turbines in dams to make electricity.

   _____

2. Steve grabbed the glass and <u>guzzled</u> all the water in it as fast as he could. When he finished drinking, he put the glass down with a sigh of relief.

   _____

3. <u>Renewable</u> forms of energy like the wind don't run out. We can keep using them forever.

   _____

4. Solar power is a promising <u>alternative</u> to fossil fuels. If we use the sun's energy instead of burning fuel, we make no pollution.

   _____

At Home: Have the student explain how he or she used the context clues above to write the definition of the underlined words.

Name _____

Words can have the **/ü/** sound, the **/ů/** sound, or the **/ū/** sound.

- These underlined spellings can stand for the **/ü/** sound:
  sp_oo_l, gr_ew_, _you_'ll, t_u_ne, m_o_ve, s_ui_t.
- These underlined spellings can stand for the **/ů/** sound:
  br_oo_ks, sh_ou_ld.
- These underlined spellings can stand for the **/ū/** sound:
  _c_ute, _u_sed, m_u_le.

Use the words in the box to identify each picture. Write your answers in the blanks. If the word has a /ü/ sound, circle it.

spool	crew	suits	stoop
wool	cookie	grew	shute

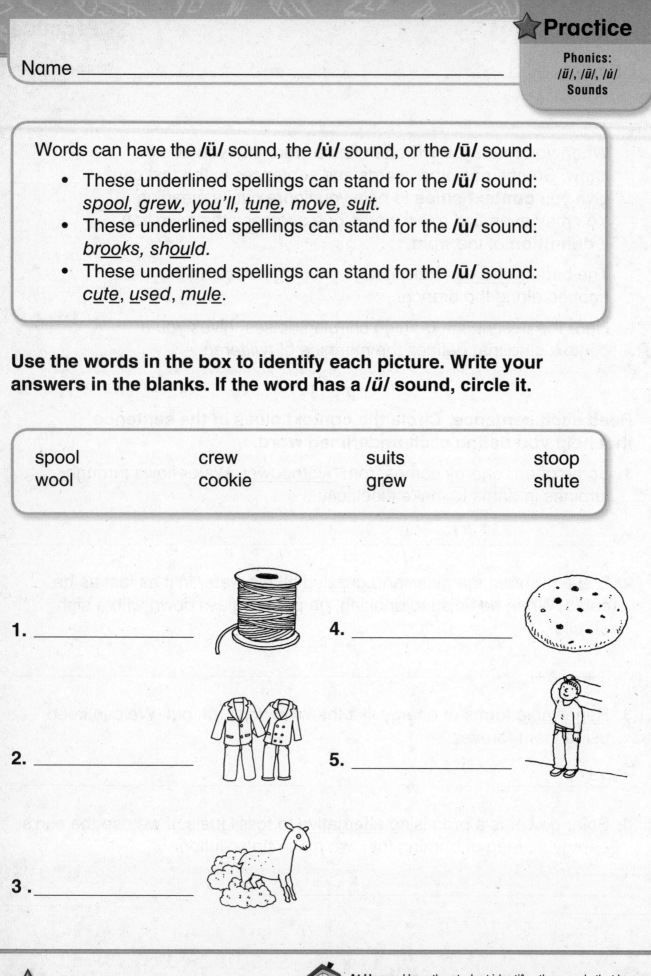

1. _____

2. _____

3. _____

4. _____

5. _____

© Macmillan/McGraw-Hill

 At Home: Have the student identify other words that have
the /ü/ sound.

Name _____

dove	politicians	snoring	massive
tangles	rumbling	unique	

**Read each clue. Then find the vocabulary word in the
row of letters and circle it.**

1. the sounds people
   make when they sleep

   l t p o r s n o r i n g v z t y r a p l o u y t w

2. threw yourself upper
   body first into the water

   l e t b s p d o v e m l k o r b s t m l p o y q

3. a deep rolling sound

   r t o l m j w r e d c h y q w r u m b l i n g

4. different from all
   the rest

   p u n i q u e g h s k l e b t y x m a l d o w

5. twisted messes

   j t a n h j f k t a n g l e s m q p t s k l p i

6. elected officials

   k u t n p o l i t i c i a n s v d y z x q p e l

7. very, very large

   n h d f l k h v b q w t m a s s i v e y g o

**Write three sentences using as many vocabulary words
as possible.**

8. _____

   _____

9. _____

   _____

10. _____

   _____

The things that happen in a story are called **events**. The order in which they happen is the **sequence**. Recognizing the **sequence of events** in a story is key to understanding it.

Each group of sentences below tells a story out of sequence. For each group, number the sentences from 1 to 4 to show the correct sequence of events.

1. ____ Then she ate her breakfast and fed the dog.

    ____ Linda grabbed her lunch and binoculars and left the house.

    ____ She walked to the pier to get on the boat for the whale watch.

    ____ Linda got up at 7:00 and brushed her teeth.

2. ____ The whale dove back under the water.

    ____ People took pictures of the whale.

    ____ The captain shouted, "There's a whale to our left!"

    ____ Everyone ran to the left side of the boat to see it.

3. ____ It was Linda who spotted the next whale.

    ____ Then it disappeared below the surface.

    ____ People hurried over in time to get good pictures of its fluke.

    ____ "Look, everybody!" she yelled. "There's another one!"

4. ____ Linda couldn't believe her eyes. "Over here, everybody!" she cried.

    ____ "When we circle that island, look towards shore," the captain said.

    ____ "Do we only get to see them when they come up for air?" Linda asked.

    ____ Four mother whales were teaching their calves how to swim.

At Home: Together with the student, recall a family party or other special event. Have him or her tell you the sequence of events in the correct order.

© Macmillan/McGraw-Hill

Name _____

As you read *Adelina's Whales,* fill in the Sequence Chart.

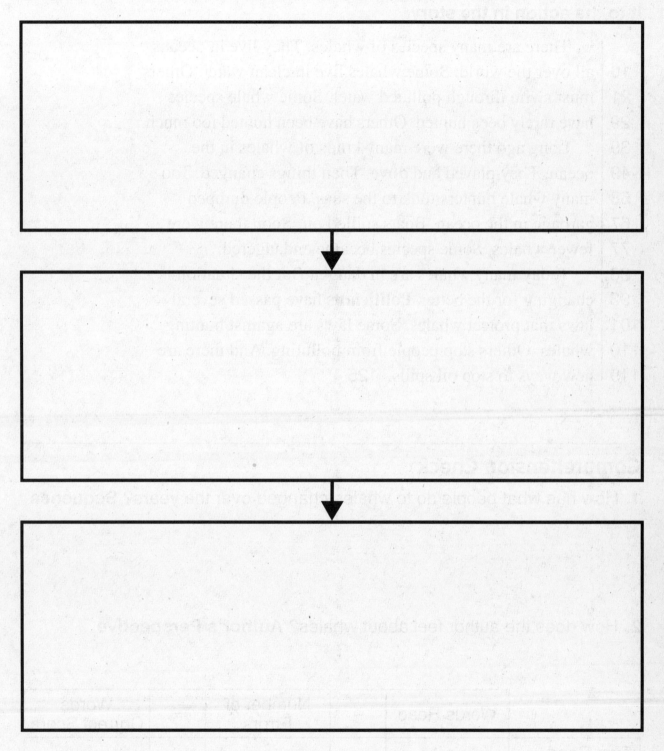

How does the information you wrote in the Sequence Chart help you to analyze the text structure of *Adelina's Whales*?

 At Home: Have the student use the chart to retell the story.

Adelina's Whales
Grade 4/Unit 4

135

© Macmillan/McGraw-Hill

As I read, I will pay attention to my tempo and try to match it to the action in the story.

	There are many species of whales. They live in oceans
10	all over the world. Some whales live in clean water. Others
21	must swim through polluted water. Some whale species
29	have rarely been hunted. Others have been hunted too much.
39	Long ago there were many kinds of whales in the
49	ocean. They played and **dove**. Then things changed. Too
58	many whale hunters took to the seas. People dumped
67	garbage in the ocean. Boats spilled oil. Soon there were
77	fewer whales. Some species became endangered.
83	Today many whales are in danger. But the situation is
93	changing for the better. **Politicians** have passed several
101	laws that protect whales. Some laws are against hunting
110	whales. Others stop people from polluting. And there are
119	new ways to stop oil spills. 125

Comprehension Check

1. How has what people do to whales changed over the years? **Sequence**

2. How does the author feel about whales? **Author's Perspective**

	Words Read	–	Number of Errors	=	Words Correct Score
First Read		–		=	
Second Read		–		=	

136 Adelina's Whales
Grade 4/Unit 4

At Home: Help the student read the passage, paying attention to the goal at the top of the page.

Name _____

Some poems have words that rhyme at the end of each line. The **rhyme scheme** is the pattern of the rhymes in the poem. You can describe rhyme schemes by giving each rhyme its own letter. Poems also have a **meter.** This is the way that syllable accents are arranged in the poem. You can think of it as the poem's rhythm.

A. Read the following limerick. Then circle the first set of three rhyming words and underline the second set of two rhyming words.

> There was a young lady whose chin,
> Resembled the point of a pin;
> So she had it made sharp,
> And purchased a harp,
> And played several tunes with her chin.
>
> — by Edward Lear

B. Read the first line of the limerick to yourself quietly. Then read the line below that describes its meter. Following the model, then write the meter for the rest of the limerick.

ba-**bum**-ba-ba-**bum**-ba-ba-**bum**

_____

_____

_____

_____

At Home: Together with the student, find two more limericks. Have him or her read the limericks out loud and identify the rhyming words.

Adelina's Whales
Grade 4/Unit 4

137

Name _____

You already know about homophones, which are words that are spelled differently but pronounced the same. **Homographs** are words that have the same spelling but different meanings. They may also be pronounced differently.

For example, *wind* pronounced with a short *i* sound means "moving air." But *wind* with a long *i* sound means "to wrap around something."

Read the homographs in the first column of the table below. Write the two meanings of the word in the second column of the table. In the third column, make a check mark to indicate whether the first or the second syllable is stressed.

Homograph	Definition	Stressed Syllable	
		First	Second
1. tear	_____ _____	—	—
		—	—
2. dove	_____ _____	—	—
		—	—
3. present	_____ _____		
4. content	_____ _____		

© Macmillan/McGraw-Hill

 At Home: Review the meanings of the above homographs with the student.

The letters *-oi* or *-oy* stand for the /oi/ sound. The letters *-ou* or *-ow* stand for the /ou/ sound.

Read the list of words below. Then read the sentences that follow. In each blank, write the word that completes the sentence. Then circle the letter pair found in each word.

coin	oyster	noise	annoy	poison
loud	bow	crowd	out	count

1. I dropped a _____ in the snack machine.

2. On the _____ of three, the coach blew the whistle to start the race.

3. As the audience clapped, the orchestra stood up and took

   a _____.

4. The flies and mosquitoes were starting to _____ me.

5. A loud _____ woke my baby brother up from his nap.

6. The _____ was safe in its shell.

7. The bottle of _____ had a bright red warning label.

8. The flying fish jumped _____ of the water.

9. The police officer spotted the lost child in the _____.

10. The _____ music was coming from my brother's room.

At Home: Together with the student, make a list of additional words that have the /oi/ and /ou/ sounds.

© Macmillan/McGraw-Hill

Name _____

| coral | reef | brittle | eventually |
| current | partnership | suburbs | |

Write a vocabulary word from the list to answer each question.

1. What is a flow of water? _____

2. What do you call it when two people work together?

   _____

3. What would you call the area outside of a city? _____

4. What is a small underwater animal with a hard skeleton outside

   its body? _____

5. How can you describe something that is easy to break?

   _____

6. What is coral or sand right under the water's surface called?

   _____

7. What word means "after a while"? _____

Choose three of the vocabulary words and use each in a sentence.

8. _____

9. _____

10. _____

© Macmillan/McGraw-Hill

Name _____

When you **compare** two things, you talk about how they are alike. When you **contrast** two things, you talk about how they are different. For example, you can compare cats and dogs by writing "Both cats and dogs are furry and have four legs." You can contrast them by writing "Dogs bark, but cats meow."

Read the paragraph. Then write *compare* next to sentences that tell how two characters are alike. Write *contrast* next to sentences that tell how they are different.

    Keisha and Donna are both scientists who study the ocean. Keisha studies sharks. Donna studies coral reefs. They both love to scuba dive for their research. Keisha also teaches classes on sharks at a college. Donna spends all her time studying the reefs and writing about what she finds.

1. _____ Keisha and Donna are both scientists who study the ocean.

2. _____ Keisha studies sharks. Donna studies coral reefs.

3. _____ They both love to scuba dive for their research.

4. _____ Keisha also teaches classes on sharks at a college. Donna spends all her time studying the reefs and writing about what she finds.

At Home: Have the student compare his or her likes and dislikes with a friend or a brother or sister.

© Macmillan/McGraw-Hill

★ **Practice**

Comprehension:
Compare and Contrast

Name _____

As you read *At Home in the Coral Reef*, fill in the Venn Diagram.

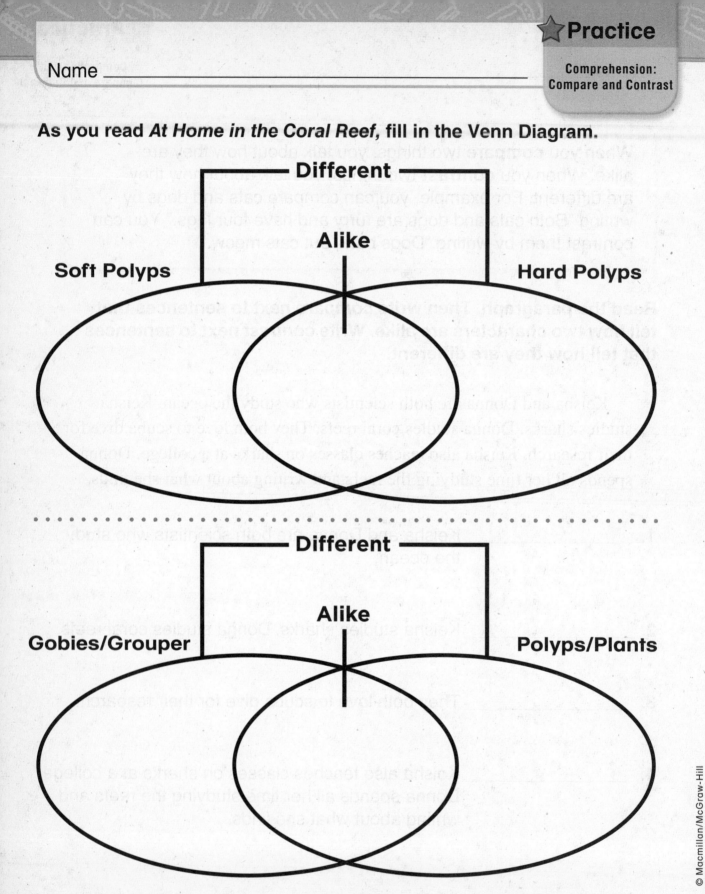

Different

Alike

Soft Polyps   **Hard Polyps**

Different

Alike

Gobies/Grouper   **Polyps/Plants**

How does completing the Venn Diagram help you to analyze the text structure of *At Home in the Coral Reef*?

142
At Home in the Coral Reef
Grade 4/Unit 4

At Home: Have the student use the chart to retell the story.

Name _____

As I read, I will pay attention to my pronunciation of vocabulary words.

	Think cold. Think very, very cold. On a visit to the Arctic Ocean,
13	you will need your warmest clothes. And you might want to leave
25	your bathing suit at home. For people, swimming is pretty much
36	out of the question. Even in the summer, the average water
47	temperature is below freezing. Three fourths of the ocean surface is
58	frozen. In the winter the entire ocean surface is frozen. Polar bears,
70	seals, and other animals live on islands made of **brittle** ice.
81	The Arctic Ocean is at the top of the world. For part of the summer,
96	the sun never sets. And for part of the winter, the sun never rises. This,
111	along with the extreme cold, makes the Arctic Ocean a tough place to
124	live or to visit. To survive, arctic plants and animals must adapt to
137	these conditions. 139

Comprehension Check

1. How is the Arctic Ocean in the summer different from the Arctic Ocean in the winter? How is the ocean the same in both seasons? **Compare and Contrast**

2. How does too little sunlight make life difficult in the Arctic? **Draw Conclusions**

	Words Read	–	Number of Errors	=	Words Correct Score
First Read		–		=	
Second Read		–		=	

© Macmillan/McGraw-Hill

 At Home: Help the student read the passage, paying attention to the goal at the top of the page.

At Home in the Coral Reef
Grade 4/Unit 4

 143

Another name for the main character is the **protagonist.**
For example, in "Poseidon and the Kingdom of Atlantis" the
protagonist is Poseidon.
When a writer exaggerates to make a point or to make things
seem more dramatic, it's called **hyperbole.** For example, if an
author writes "The water was so cold that my finger froze solid
when I dipped it in," he or she is using hyperbole.

**Read the passage below. Then circle the answers to the
questions that follow.**

　　Dina was looking forward to going to the aquarium. "I've been waiting
for a thousand years!" she told her mother. Finally the day of her class
field trip came. They waited in line for tickets. "This line must be at least
two miles long," Dina said. Before long they had their tickets and went
into the aquarium. They passed a tank with a big shark swimming in it.
"Wow—he's big enough to bite a boat in half!" Dina almost shouted.
　　"Actually his mouth is very small," said Tyra, one of her classmates.
　　"Oh," answered Dina. "I bet it's smaller than a speck of dust."

1. Who is the protagonist in this story?

a. Dina

b. Tyra

**For each pair of sentences, circle the letter of the one that
includes hyperbole.**

2. a. Dina was looking forward to going to the aquarium.

b. "I've been waiting for a thousand years!" she told her mother.

3. a. "This line must be at least two miles long," Dina said.

b. They waited in line for tickets.

4. a. "Wow—he's big enough to bite a boat in half!" Dina almost shouted.

b. "Actually his mouth is very small," said Tyra, one of her classmates.

At Home: Ask the student to come up with his or her own
example of hyperbole. Then ask him or her to say the same
thing without using exaggeration.

When you read, you will often find a word that you do not know. Sometimes these unfamiliar words are described in surrounding text. These descriptions often provide **context clues** to help you figure out the meaning of the unfamiliar word.

Example: The water was <u>choppy,</u> with small waves that slammed against the boat.

Here the description in the second part of the sentence can help you to figure out that *choppy* is a word that describes rough water.

Read each sentence. Circle the correct meaning of the word in bold. Underline the context clues that helped you figure out the meaning.

1. The **grubby** dog needed a bath after playing on the beach.

   a. clean   **b.** dirty

2. My mother made a big **feast** for the party that included salad and chicken wings.

   a. special meal   **b.** gift

3. The **miniature** shark made the other sharks look huge.

   a. with sharp teeth   **b.** very small

4. The boat **lurched** to the right when I turned the steering wheel.

   a. leaned hard to one side   b. floated

5. The **seashore** was full of kids swimming in the ocean and playing on the sand.

   a. swimming pool   **b.** beach

At Home: Together with the student, read a magazine article and use context clues to figure out the meaning of unfamiliar words.

The **/ô/** sound is the sound you hear in words like **small** and **fought**.
There are several different spellings that can stand for this sound.
- **a** as in *ba̲ld*. Notice that in this word, you pronounce the **l**.
- **al** as in *sta̲lk*. Notice that in this word, you do not pronounce the **l**.
- **aw** as in *stra̲w*
- **au** as in *ca̲ught*

For each word, circle the letters that stand for the /ô/ sound.

1. walk

2. taught

3. ball

4. lawn

5. gawk

6. hall

7. awful

8. launch

9. talking

10. laws

At Home: Together with the student, think of three other
words that have the /ô/ sound.

© Macmillan/McGraw-Hill

Name _____

A. Write a word from the box to complete each sentence.

| rumbling | faint | desperate | cautiously | coral |

1. Jon ran as fast as he could. He was _____ to win the race.

2. I knew the train was coming because I could feel the ground _____ under my feet.

3. The _____ sound of bells could be heard in the distance.

4. Her favorite part of the scuba dive was seeing all of the _____ growing.

5. Sara walked _____ on the ice so she wouldn't slip.

B. Read each question. Choose a word from the box to answer the question. Write your answer on the line.

| reef | brittle | globe | obedience | neglected |

6. When your fingernails get dry and hard, what are they?

_____

7. If a dog does as he is told, what is he showing? _____

8. How might you feel if you were ignored and not taken care of?

_____

9. What word names an ecosystem of coral and other animals under the

surface of the water? _____

10. What is a word that describes the shape of the Earth? _____

© Macmillan/McGraw-Hill

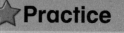
Name _____

C. Draw a line to match the word to its definition.

11. snoring   **a.** making a low, rolling noise

12. tourists   **b.** wanting what someone else has

13. rumbling   **c.** useful knowledge, usually based on experience

14. wisdom   **d.** making noisy sounds in one's sleep

15. jealousy   **e.** people who visit places they are not from

D. Finish each sentence with a word from the box.

fade	fuels	risks	tangles	decayed

16. Coal and oil are examples of _____ that make energy or heat.

17. A synonym for the word *rotted* is _____.

18. It wasn't easy to comb the _____ out of Jack's long, shaggy coat.

19. The sound of the ocean waves began to _____ as we walked back to the house.

20. There are a lot of _____ involved in scuba diving, so I had to pass a diving test.

Name _____

| snuffled | selecting | positive |
| consisted | peculiar | advanced |

Read each clue. Then find the vocabulary word and draw a line to it.

1. choosing   a. snuffled

2. sure   b. advanced

3. strange   c. consisted

4. at a high level   d. peculiar

5. made of   e. selecting

6. sniffed loudly   f. positive

Write the correct vocabulary word in the blank.

7. Lunch _____ of salad, pizza, juice, and fruit.

8. Lee felt proud to be reading at an _____ level.

9. Read the first pages when you are _____ books in the library if you want to be sure you get ones you will enjoy.

10. The bear looked sadly out of its cage and _____ loudly.

11. I was _____ that my new neighbor's name was Lucinda.

12. She gave me the most _____ look when I called her that, though.

Name _____

> A **summary** is a short retelling of what you've read. When you
> **summarize,** include only the most important ideas, and be sure to
> use your own words.

**Read each passage below. Then circle the answer that gives
the best summary.**

1. Many libraries have computers. You can use these computers to find
the books you need. Some library computers can go online. These
computers can help you find information you need to do your homework.
Many people want to use the computers, so there is usually a time limit
on how long you can use them. You need to take turns and be fair.

   a. You need to take turns when you use a computer. You may have a time
   limit on using a library computer.

   b. Library computers can help people find books, get information for
   homework, and sometimes go online. Most library computers limit
   users' time.

   c. You can also request books on-line. Log in on the library's website.
   Then find the books you need. Your books will be waiting for you at
   the Check-out Desk.

2. To check out books, bring your books and your library card to the
checkout desk. The librarian will record the date you borrowed the
books. He or she will also tell you when you should return the books. At
many libraries, the date to return your books may be stamped inside the
books' covers.

   a. There are many different books at the library. The librarian's job is to
   record dates when books are borrowed. The date to return your book
   may be stamped inside the book.

   b. To check out books, take your library card and books to the checkout
   desk. The librarian will tell you when to bring the books back.

   c. Many libraries have computers.

© Macmillan/McGraw-Hill

At Home: Summarize a favorite story with the
student. Be sure that he or she includes only the most
important information.

As you read *Because of Winn-Dixie*, fill in the Summarizing Chart.

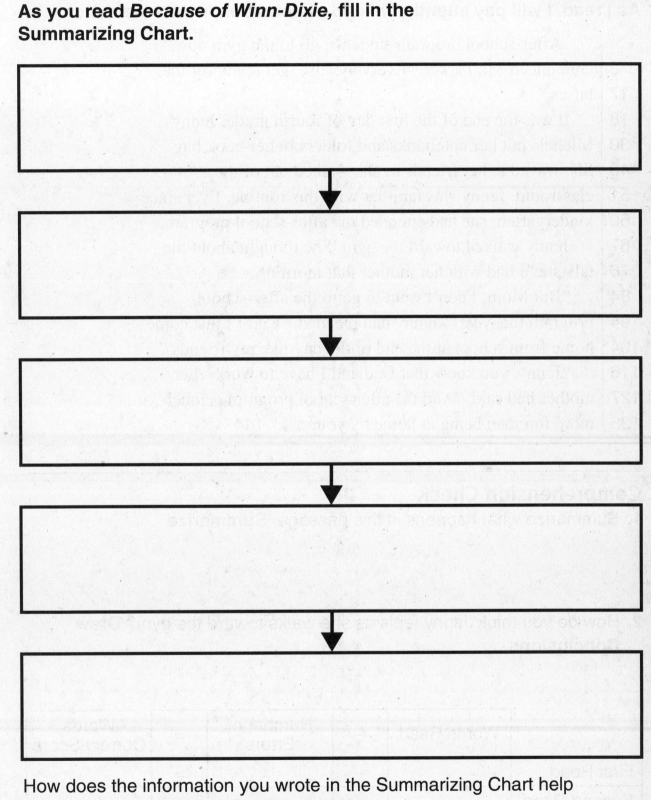

How does the information you wrote in the Summarizing Chart help
you to evaluate *Because of Winn-Dixie*?

 At Home: Have the student use the chart to retell the story.

Because of Winn-Dixie
Grade 4/Unit 5

 151

© Macmillan/McGraw-Hill

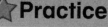
Name _____

As I read, I will pay attention to end punctuation in each sentence.

8	"After-school program students, go to the gym now," announced Mr. Parker. "Everyone else, get ready for the
17	buses."
18	It was the end of the first day of fourth grade. Jenny
30	Michels put her notebooks and folders in her book bag.
40	She waved at her friends as she walked out of the
51	classroom. Jenny was familiar with this routine. Ever since
60	kindergarten, she had attended the after-school program.
67	Jenny walked toward the gym. She thought about the
76	talk she'd had with her mother that morning.
84	"But Mom, I don't want to go to the after-school
94	program this year!" Jenny had pleaded. "Can't I just come
104	home from school at the end of the day like my friends?"
116	"Jenny, you know that Dad and I have to work," her
127	mother had said. "And the after-school program is much
136	more fun than being at home by yourself." 144

Comprehension Check

1. Summarize what happens in this passage. **Summarize**

2. How do you think Jenny feels as she walks toward the gym? **Draw Conclusions**

	Words Read	−	Number of Errors	=	Words Correct Score
First Read		−		=	
Second Read		−		=	

© Macmillan/McGraw-Hill

At Home: Help the student read the passage, paying attention to the goal at the top of the page.

Onomatopoeia is the use of a word that imitates the sound that it stands for. For example, the word *bang* sounds a lot like the noise an explosion makes.

A **simile** compares two things. Similes use the word *like, as,* or *than* to make a comparison. In the sentence, *I can run as fast as the wind,* you're using a simile to compare the speed of running and the wind.

Read the poem below. Then answer the questions that follow.

At the Library

The kids at the next table are talking loud—*yak, yak yak*
Noisy as a flock of birds, without even stopping long enough
To take a breath.
I feel the librarian glide past me
Like a jaguar in the jungle.
He pounces,
And shushes them.

1. Which word is an example of onomatopoeia?

   a. kids   **b.** yak   **c.** birds

2. To what does the poet compare the talking kids?

   a. a flock of birds   **b.** the librarian   **c.** a jaguar

3. What word does the poet use to compare the librarian to a jaguar?

   a. *like*   **b.** *as*   **c.** *than*

4. What other word in the poem is an example of onomatopoeia?

   a. *feel*   **b.** *next*   **c.** *shushes*

At Home: With the student, name as many examples of
onomatopoeia as you can.

Because of Winn-Dixie
Grade 4/Unit 5

153

© Macmillan/McGraw-Hill

> Think about the picture you see when you read the word *drink*.
> Now think about the picture the word *gulp* creates.
> *Drink* and *gulp* have similar meanings but each word creates a
> different feeling or picture.
> - The dictionary meaning of a word is its **denotation**.
> - The feelings connected to a word are its **connotation**.
> A word can have a good or bad connnotation.

**Read the sentences below carefully. In the blank, write the word
from the parentheses that best completes the sentence. Take into
account the connotation of the word.**

1. The temperature was so low and the wind so strong, that even in

   my heavy coat I was _____ (freezing, chilly).

2. I won't say I was excited to get home, but I was _____
   (overjoyed, happy).

3. It helps to be _____ (tall, gigantic) if you want to
   play basketball.

4. Justin is careful with his money. I admire him for being

   _____ (thrifty, stingy).

5. Carmen could hardly see it, but she was able to pick up the

   _____ (minuscule, small) part with a pair of tweezers.

6. In the summertime, the _____ (aroma, stench) of the
   landfill forced us to close our classroom's windows.

At Home: With the student, discuss whether each answer
above has a good or bad connotation.

Name _____

Dividing a word into **syllables** can help you read the word.
A two-syllable word with the **VCCV pattern** is usually divided
between the two consonants.

| better | bet / ter |
| basket | bas / ket |

The first syllable of a VCCV word is a **closed** syllable. That means
it has a short vowel sound and ends in a consonant.

**Read each word. Circle the example that shows the word
correctly divided into syllables.**

1. willow   **a.** wil / low   **b.** will / ow

2. dipper   **a.** di / pper   **b.** dip / per

3. blossom   **a.** blo / ssom   **b.** blos / som

4. dinner   **a.** din / ner   **b.** dinn / er

5. plastic   **a.** plas / tic   **b.** plast / ic

6. seldom   **a.** se / ldom   **b.** sel / dom

7. darkest   **a.** dar / kest   **b.** dark / est

8. wetness   **a.** we / tness   **b.** wet / ness

9. perfect   **a.** perf / ect   **b.** per / fect

10. garlic   **a.** gar / lic   **b.** garl / ic

© Macmillan/McGraw-Hill

At Home: Ask the student to divide the following closed-
syllable words: *planner, nodded, engine.*

cranky	bumbling	selfish	exasperated
specialty	famished	commotion	

Write the vocabulary word that best fits each clue.

1. eating more than your share _____

2. clumsy _____

3. annoyed and frustrated _____

4. lots of noise and activity _____

5. an uncommon ability or product _____

6. very hungry _____

7. easily irritated _____

Write the vocabulary word that best fits the blank in each sentence.

8. Siri was so busy that she skipped lunch, and by 5 o'clock she was

_____.

9. There was such a _____ in the dining hall that I couldn't hear myself think.

10. The _____ waiter dropped a glass and then poked a customer with a broom while trying to clean it up.

11. That was so _____ ! There were only five slices of pizza left, and Dave and Dana took four of them.

12. It's not something that many people still do nowadays, but baking bread is my _____.

Name _____

When you read, you form opinions, or **make judgments**, about the characters in the story. What the characters do and say help you make judgments.

> Ella bumped into Tim and knocked his lunch to the floor.
> "Hey, don't worry about it," Tim said. "Accidents happen."

The way Tim reacted to the accident helps you make the judgment that Tim is kind, or that he doesn't get mad easily.

Read the passage below and make judgments as you read. Then answer the questions that follow.

The fourth grade class was putting on a play. "I want to make scenery," Josh said. "I know how to paint, and I can use a saw."

Mrs. Hartman, the teacher, said there would be tryouts for each part. "That way, everyone will have a chance," she explained.

Most of the girls wanted to try out for the part of the princess, but Conchita wanted to try out for the evil stepmother. "It will be fun to pretend to be such a bad person," she said.

After six girls tried out for the part of the princess, the class voted. They chose Ariana. She had read her lines in a clear voice with a lot of expression.

1. What judgment can you make about Josh? He is

   a. friendly   **b.** confident   **c.** cranky

2. What kind of person is Mrs. Hartman?

   a. unfair   **b.** confusing   **c.** fair

3. Which word best describes Conchita?

   a. mean   **b.** sneaky   **c.** adventurous

4. Why did Ariana get the most votes?

   a. She was a good actress.   **b.** She was pretty.   **c.** Everyone liked her.

At Home: Together, discuss the student's favorite story character. Make judgments about that character based on how he or she acts in the story.

Ranita, the Frog Princess
Grade 4/Unit 5

© Macmillan/McGraw-Hill

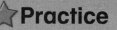

**As you read *Ranita, the Frog Princess*, fill in the
Make Judgments Flow Chart.**

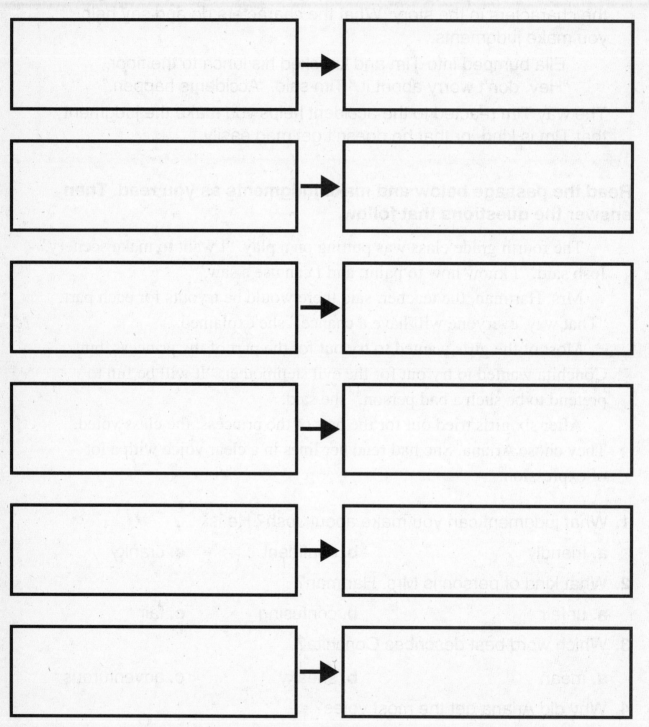

How does the information you wrote in the Make Judgments Flow Chart
help you to evaluate *Ranita, the Frog Princess*?

 At Home: Have the student use the chart to retell the story.

© Macmillan/McGraw-Hill

As I read, I will pay attention to dialogue and characters' roles.

11	*[Hans and Greta are walking through the woods. They are going*
21	*to Grandma Maggie's house. As they walk they eat sandwiches,*
31	*leaving a trail of crumbs. Their stepmother and father stand*
34	*together, waving good-bye.]*
43	**Stepmother:** Good-bye! Be sure to go straight to Grandma
47	Maggie's. Don't get lost.
58	**Father:** (*smiling and shaking his head*) If they get lost, they
69	can always follow the trail of crumbs back to our house.
80	**Stepmother:** (*nods her head, then shakes a finger at Hans and*
90	*Greta*) And don't play any of your tricks on Grandma.
98	**Hans and Greta:** We won't, Stepmother. Good-bye, Father!
110	*[Hans and Greta walk a little farther, then look at each other*
112	*and laugh.]*
123	**Greta:** I won't play tricks on Grandma Maggie. I'll play them
	on the Cat. 126

Comprehension Check

1. What inferences can you make about Hans and Greta? **Make Inferences**

2. What problem might the children face and how does the father suggest they solve it? **Problem and Solution**

	Words Read	−	Number of Errors	=	Words Correct Score
First Read		−		=	
Second Read		−		=	

© Macmillan/McGraw-Hill

At Home: Help the student read the passage, paying attention to the goal at the top of the page.

Ranita, the Frog Princess
Grade 4/Unit 5

Name _____

In an **interview, questions** are asked by one person and **answered** by another. Interviews are conversations between two people that have been written down for others to read.

The following is part of an interview with a fourth-grader who works "behind the scenes" at his local community theater. Read the interview and then answer the questions that follow.

Q: What's involved in making scenery, Stephanie?

A: More than people think. First the set has to be designed. Then it has to be painted. Finally it has to be put into place. If there is more than one scene, the whole process has to be repeated for each additional scene.

Q: How did you get involved in working on the sets?

A: I always liked going to plays, but I don't like being on stage. This way I can still be part of the performance but stay in the background.

Q: How long have you been with the community theater?

A: I've been making scenery and props for about 2 years.

1. Who is being interviewed?

_____

2. How long has Stephanie worked with the community theater?

_____

3. Why doesn't Stephanie perform on stage?

_____

4. How does Stephanie help out at the theater?

_____

© Macmillan/McGraw-Hill

Ranita, the Frog Princess
Grade 4/Unit 5
160

At Home: Conduct an interview with the student. Take turns asking and answering questions about a favorite activity.

Name _____

Words that have opposite meanings are called **antonyms.**
You can find out if a word has an antonym by looking in
a **thesaurus**. A thesaurus is a book that lists words in
alphabetical order. Following each word is a list of
its synonyms and antonyms.

| peacefulness content stuffed greedy upset obeyed |

Read each sentence. Choose an antonym for the underlined word(s) from the list above.

1. I thought he was being <u>generous</u>, but he was actually being

   _____.

2. By the time dinner was served, I was so <u>hungry</u> that I ate until

   I was _____.

3. After all the <u>racket</u> died down, the neighborhood returned to

   _____.

4. Mario was so <u>unhappy</u> that his friends wondered if he would ever be

   _____ again.

5. Juan <u>refused</u> to follow the order, but his friend Erik _____.

6. Caterina remained <u>calm</u> even though her friends were very

   _____.

At Home: Together, name an antonym for the word *friendly,*
peace, or *happiness.*

Ranita, the Frog Princess
Grade 4/Unit 5

161

© Macmillan/McGraw-Hill

Name _____

An **open syllable** ends with a long vowel sound. Words with open first syllables have the **V/CV pattern**.
The first syllable in *razor* ends with a long **a** sound, so it is an open syllable.

   ra / zor

A **closed syllable** ends with a consonant. The vowel sound is short. Words with closed first syllables have the **VC/V pattern**.
The first syllable in *level* ends with a consonant and has a short **e** vowel sound. It is a closed syllable.

   lev / el

Read each word and listen for the vowel sound in the first syllable. Circle the word that shows the correct syllable pattern.

1. cabin	ca / bin	cab / in
2. petal	pe / tal	pet / al
3. diver	di / ver	div / er
4. finish	fi / nish	fin / ish
5. motor	mo / tor	mot / or
6. tiger	ti / ger	tig / er
7. habit	ha / bit	hab / it
8. wiper	wi / per	wip / er
9. spoken	spo / ken	spok / en
10. never	ne / ver	nev / er

© Macmillan/McGraw-Hill

 At Home: Together, divide the following words into syllables: *camel, spider, crater, habit.*

Name _____

Answer each question with a vocabulary word from the box.

| period | vessels | valuable | documenting | estimated |

1. What do sea-going sailors travel in? _____

2. What word means the same as "worth a lot of money"?

   _____

3. What does the term "Jurassic" refer to? a _____ of time

4. When a recorder is writing down what is said at a meeting, what is she

   or he doing? _____

5. If you made an educated guess about a quantity, what did you do?

   _____

Read each vocabulary word. Then draw a line from the word to its definition.

6. period   taking notes

7. vessels   approximated

8. valuable   ships

9. documenting   span

10. estimated   priceless

Name _____

> A **fact** is a statement that can be proven true.
>   *There are 50 states In the United States.*
> An **opinion** is a statement that tells what a person thinks or feels about something. An opinion cannot be proven true.
>   *Idaho is the most beautiful state in our country.*

Read each statement. If it is a fact, circle "fact." If the statement is an opinion that cannot be proven, circle "opinion."

1. I think that exploration will always be viewed as important.

    fact   opinion

2. Years ago, explorers traveled to new lands.

    fact   opinion

3. Explorers often brought lots of riches back to their native countries.

    fact   opinion

4. We should only explore the oceans.

    fact   opinion

5. Water covers most of the world.

    fact   opinion

6. Machu Picchu was known as the lost city of the Incan empire.

    fact   opinion

7. Finding Machu Picchu is the greatest archaeological discovery of all time.

    fact   opinion

8. The exploration of space is an enormous waste of time and money.

    fact   opinion

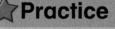

© Macmillan/McGraw-Hill

At Home: With the student, identify facts and opinions while listening to the news on the television or radio.

Name _____

As you read *Exploring the Undersea Territory,* fill in the Fact and Opinion Chart.

Facts	Opinions

How does the information you wrote in the Fact and Opinion Chart help you to evaluate *Exploring the Undersea Territory*?

At Home: Have the student use the chart to retell the story.

© Macmillan/McGraw-Hill

As I read, I will pay attention to my pronunciation of vocabulary words and other difficult words.

	Fish swim in almost every body of water in the
10	world. Some are freshwater fish, and others are saltwater
19	fish. Herbivorous (hur-BIV-uh-ruhs) fish eat only grasses
26	and other plants. Carnivorous (kahr-NIV-uh-ruhs) fish eat
33	other fish and animals.
37	Some fish are small and docile, such as minnows. Other
47	fish are large predators, such as sharks. Some fish give
57	birth to live baby fish, and others lay eggs. Scientists
67	estimate that there are over 20,000 species of fish in all,
77	and those are just the ones we know about.
86	What is a fish, anyway? Fish are vertebrate animals.
95	That means that they have backbones. Fish are
103	cold-blooded creatures, and most breathe using gills.
110	They have swum on our planet for about 500 million
119	years.
120	There are three main kinds of fish: jawless,
128	cartilaginous, and bony. 131

Comprehension Check

1. Why did the author write this passage? **Author's Purpose**

2. How are herbivorous and carnivorous fish alike and different?
Compare and Contrast

	Words Read	−	Number of Errors	=	Words Correct Score
First Read		−		=	
Second Read		−		=	

At Home: Help the student read the passage, paying attention to the goal at the top of the page.

Name _____

When you **skim,** you quickly look through a portion of the text to find out its main idea and supporting details. When you are doing research, it is helpful to skim the Table of Contents of a book to see whether it has the information you need for the topic.
When you **scan,** you run through a text looking for a word or phrase. One example of scanning is when you look for an entry in the dictionary.

Decide whether you would skim or scan a passage to find the following information.

1. a detail for a main idea _____

2. the word *explorer* _____

3. which character in a story says, "That's not my dog!" _____

4. what a selection is about _____

5. the dictionary entry for *undersea* _____

6. the date July 4, 1776 in a Social Studies book _____

7. whether a nonfiction book can help you write a report _____

8. how challenging a novel will be to read _____

9. the place where you stopped reading before _____

10. how many lines your character has in the play _____

11. whether you'd be interested in reading a book _____

12. where a vocabulary word is used in a story _____

At Home: Together with the student, skim a section of one of his or her textbooks and describe the information it contains.

An **analogy** compares two pairs of words. For the analogy to
make sense, the words in each pair must be related to each
other in the same way. For example, if the words in one pair are
synonyms, the words in the second pair must be synonyms.
Example: *Big* is to *large* as *little* is to *small*.

Choose the word that best completes each analogy.

1. *Flying* is to *bird* as *swimming* is to ____.

   a. *fish*   **b.** *diving*

2. *Tiger* is to *animal* as *oak* is to ____.

   a. *maple*   **b.** *tree*

3. *Over* is to *under* as *hot* is to ____.

   a. *cold*   **b.** *burning*

4. *Nighttime* is to *dark* as *daytime* is to ____.

   a. *light*   **b.** *noon*

5. *Swim* is to *lake* as *run* is to ____.

   a. *jog*   **b.** *track*

6. *Elena* is to *first name* as *Rosenthal* is to ____.

   a. *last name*   **b.** *Miguel*

7. *Bicep* is to *muscle* as *rib* is to ____.

   a. *pelvis*   **b.** *bone*

8. *You're welcome* is to *Thank you* as *Well, thank you. And you?* is to ____.

   a. *How do you do?*   **b.** *How are you?*

 At Home: Together, review the above analogies. Discuss
the relationship between each pair of words.

In a two-syllable word, one syllable is said with more emphasis, or stress. For example, in the word *friendly,* the accent, or stress, is on the first syllable.

Word	1st Syllable	2nd Syllable
friendly	**friend**	ly
confused	con	**fused**

If you are not sure which syllable in a word is accented, first try saying the word with the accent on the first syllable. If that doesn't sound right, say the word with the accent on the second syllable. Of course, you can always look in a dictionary to find out which syllable is stressed.

Say each word to yourself. Then circle the accented syllable.

1. report	re port		9. direct	di rect
2. above	a bove		10. window	win dow
3. insect	in sect		11. thunder	thun der
4. unfold	un fold		12. border	bor der
5. ocean	o cean		13. birthplace	birth place
6. below	be low		14. giraffe	gi raffe
7. limit	lim it		15. crackle	crack le
8. constant	con stant		16. accent	ac cent

Write four more.

17. _____ _____

18. _____ _____

19. _____ _____

20. _____ _____

© Macmillan/McGraw-Hill

At Home: Together, identify the accented syllable in the student's first or last name.

Exploring the Undersea Territory
Grade 4/Unit 5

169

Name _____

| strutting | swarms | flicked | barbecue |
| skyscrapers | glorious | collage | |

Use a vocabulary word to complete each sentence.

1. I enjoy eating hotdogs and hamburgers at a _____.

2. The sun was shining and the air was warm. It was a

   _____ summer day.

3. I made a _____ using leaves, fabric, and string.

4. The _____ downtown are the tallest buildings I have
   ever seen.

5. _____ of bees buzzed around the new blossoms.

6. The horse _____ its tail to shoo away the flies.

7. I watched the rooster _____ across the barnyard.

**Choose three vocabulary words and use each of them in
a sentence.**

8. _____

   _____

9. _____

   _____

10. _____

   _____

© Macmillan/McGraw-Hill

> **Characters** are the people you read about in a story. The main character is the most important character in the story. Readers can learn about a main character by paying attention to what the character does, says, and feels.

Read the passage below. Then answer the questions that follow.

Nancy's class was planning a trip to an art museum in the city. Nancy said, "I can hardly wait to go." She loved paintings, and had art posters all over the room she shared with her sister.

"I don't see why you're so excited about a museum," her friend Tyler commented to her.

"Original paintings are awesome," Nancy said. "You have to see them framed and on display to understand."

Finally, the day of the trip came. The school bus took almost two hours to get to the museum. Nancy and her classmates spent the whole afternoon wandering through the halls, studying the art.

At the end of the day, Tyler said to Nancy, "Now I get it. Original paintings by famous artists *are* awesome."

1. Who are the main characters in the story? _____

2. Circle the best description of Nancy.

  a. loves to paint   **b.** loves paintings   **c.** doesn't like museums

3. Circle the best description of Tyler.

  a. didn't like museums   **b.** hates the city   **c.** loves paintings

4. Which character changed in the course of the passage?

  a. Nancy   **b.** Nancy's sister   **c.** Tyler

5. What caused the change?

  a. the trip to the museum   **b.** the school bus   **c.** Nancy

At Home: Together with the student, discuss the characters in a favorite story. Talk about what the character does, says, and feels to help readers understand him or her.

Me and Uncle Romie
Grade 4/Unit 5

171

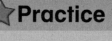
Name _____

As you read *Me and Uncle Romie*, fill in the Character Web.

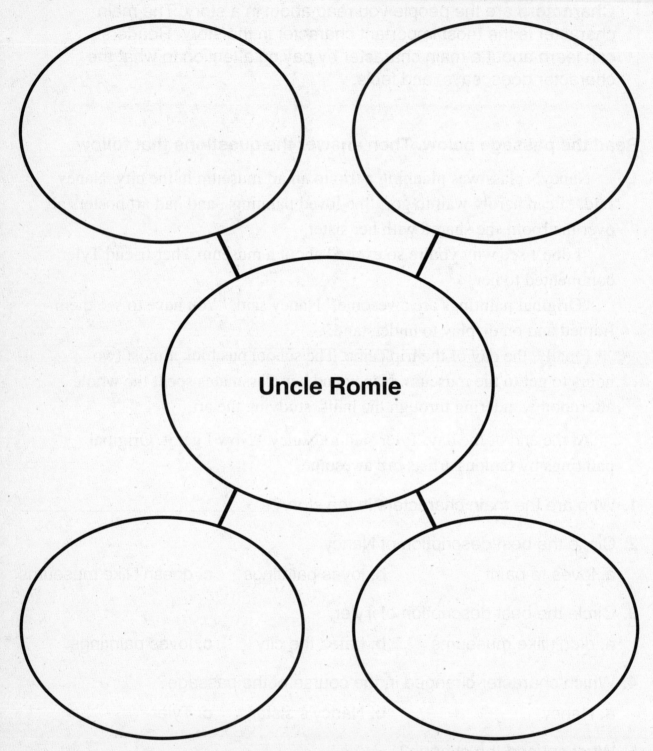

Uncle Romie

How does the information you wrote in the Character Web help you to monitor your comprehension of *Me and Uncle Romie*?

 At Home: Have the student use the chart to retell the story.

As I read, I will pay attention to my tempo in order to match the action in the story.

	"Me?" asked Louise. "She asked for me?"
7	"Yes, Louise," said her mother, smiling. "Madame
14	Cassatt wants you to model for a painting. Will you do it?"
26	Louise could not have been more surprised. She didn't
35	think anyone would want to paint a picture of her. After
46	all, she was not at all like the beautiful women usually
57	found in paintings. She was just a fourteen-year-old girl.
66	"You know Madame Cassatt," said her mother. "She is
75	the American. She comes to the bakery almost every day."
85	"Oh," said Louise, nodding. "The tall lady?"
92	"Yes," said her mother. "What should we tell her? It is
103	all right with Papa and me. Madame Cassatt is honest.
113	She can be trusted. Of course it is your decision. She has
125	offered to pay." Her mother paused. "We could
133	pay for your lessons with the singing master." 141

Comprehension Check

1. How can you tell that Louise is not stuck up or vain? **Character**

2. What opportunity has Louise been offered? **Summarize**

	Words Read	−	Number of Errors	=	Words Correct Score
First Read		−		=	
Second Read		−		=	

At Home: Help the student read the passage, paying attention to the goal at the top of the page.

> **Directions** explain how to do a task. Most directions include a list of the **materials** that you will need. They will also provide a numbered list of the **steps** that you need follow.

Read the instructions for how to use a paint-by-numbers set. Then answer the questions that follow.

Materials

paintbrush

cup of water

red, green, and yellow paint

blank paint-by-numbers picture

Directions

1. Place the picture on a flat surface.

2. Dip the paintbrush into the water.

3. Use the yellow paint to fill in areas labeled number 1. Then rinse the brush.

4. Use the green paint to fill in areas labeled number 2. Rinse the brush.

5. Use the red paint to fill in areas labeled number 3. Wash the brush.

6. Let the painting dry.

---

1. How many steps are there in the directions? ____

2. Which numbered areas should be filled in with green paint? ____

3. Put an X over the item that is not listed in the **Materials** section.

   a. paintbrush   **b.** cup full of water   **c.** blue paint   **d.** yellow paint

4. What is the last step in the directions? _____

At Home: Together, write a set of directions for "How to Brush Your Teeth."

© Macmillan/McGraw-Hill

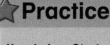
When you read, you will often come across an unfamiliar word. Sometimes, the words and sentences around the unfamiliar word can give you **context clues** to help you figure out its meaning. The clues might come in the form of a description.

For each sentence below, circle the correct meaning of the word in dark type and underline the description that provided you with a context clue.

1. The **gallery** displayed paintings by many artists. Some were already sold, and many were still for sale.

   a. a place that sells art   **b.** a home for artists   **c.** a kind of museum

2. The skyscrapers **towered** above the rest of the city.

   a. rose high   **b.** had offices in them   **c.** darkened

3. The sky **dimmed** as the sun went down.

   a. was blue   **b.** grew darker   **c.** grew brighter

4. The charm **detached** from the bracelet and fell on the floor.

   a. sparkled   **b.** stuck to   **c.** came off of

5. The gallery **rejected** the new paintings and sent them back to the artist.

   a. opened   **b.** refused to accept   **c.** displayed

6. No one could explain Chandra's **uncanny** talent for knowing when her twin in Houston was upset.

   a. mysterious   **b.** well-known   **c.** related to twins

7. Until the day he did it himself, Jeremy would laugh and consider it **ludicrous** to wear two different colored socks to school.

   a. colorblind   **b.** laughably ridiculous   **c.** superstitious

8. The biologist was studying a **protozoan** similar to the amoeba under the microscope.

   a. blood sample   **b.** virus   **c.** single-celled animal

At Home: Together, rewrite two of the above sentences with new context clues for the bold words.

© Macmillan/McGraw-Hill

Name _____

> The sound you hear at the end of *singer* is the *ər* sound.
> This sound can be spelled in several ways:
> • **ar** as in *stell<u>ar</u>*
> • **er** as in *zipp<u>er</u>*
> • **or** as in *lab<u>or</u>*
> The phonetic spelling of this sound is always *ər*.

Read each sentence. Circle the words that have the *ər* sound.

1. The artist specializes in painting river scenes that include a tanker, or container ship.

2. Mom made ham and cheddar sandwiches for our trip to the harbor.

3. We had to ring a buzzer to get into the art studio.

4. My dad used a razor to cut photographs for his collage.

5. The local dancer will answer questions after the performance.

6. I'm going to a tutor to get help with math.

7. At the first sign of danger, Captain Rogers gave the order for the anchor to be raised.

8. The barber's daughter was stuck in the skyscraper's elevator for four hours.

9. After the fourth graders studied polar bears and walruses, their instructor had them read a newsletter article and make a poster.

10. The twenty-dollar collar might be popular, but my clever cocker spaniel could always wiggle out of it.

11. The grocer told the waiter that the store didn't have any more ginger powder.

12. The train conductor tapped the passenger's shoulder, rousing her from slumber, to see whether she had a ticket for Boulder.

At Home: Ask the student to identify the different spellings of the *ər* sound in the words above.

Name _____

A. Read each clue. Then find the vocabulary word in the row of letters that best fits the clue and circle it.

descendants	habitat	threatened	sanctuary
coaxing	fragile	glistening	

1. grandchildren   l a b d e s c e n d a n t s b x e r

2. natural living area   f r e t h a b i t a t g t h b a t s

3. endangered   t h r e a t e n e d h t e r p h i n

4. safe place   g a r t t i p x s a n c t u a r y

5. persuading   b a t f e r c c o a x i n g y o u p

6. delicate   e c r f r a g i l e t r a n g e m l

7. sparkling   t e f j i n j g l i s t e n i n g s a t

B. Read the sentences below. Then edit them by crossing out the words that can be substituted with a vocabulary word. Write that word on the line.

8. I completed our family tree with my parents in the center. First, I filled in the names of their ancestors. Then I filled in the names of their children

and grandchildren. _____

9. On safari you can see wildlife in their own natural place where they live.

_____

10. I spent the whole afternoon saying, "Please, Mom, please?" and giving

lots of good reasons for Mom to change her mind. _____

A **cause** is the reason why something happens. An **effect** is what happens because of the cause. When you're looking at causes and effects, think of two questions:
- "Why did this happen?" The answer to this question is the cause.
- "What happened?" The answer to this question is the effect.

Read each sentence. Write *cause* in front of each cause and *effect* in front of each effect.

1. _____ Because of the rain, _____ I could not see my hand in front of me.

2. _____ The new fences _____ keep the horses from leaving the pasture.

3. _____ Good weather has resulted in _____ an oversupply of produce.

4. _____ The government's programs _____ have helped to protect wild horses.

5. _____ A horse sanctuary was created _____ because of one man's dream.

6. _____ We figured out that it was the raccoons

_____ that were making a mess of our garbage.

7. _____There was no electricity for four hours

_____ because a squirrel had damaged a power line.

8. _____ We finally spotted a herd of wild horses

_____ when we went to the north shore of the island.

At Home: Ask the student questions such as this: *If I plug the bath and leave the water running, what will happen?* Together, identify the missing cause or effect.

© Macmillan/McGraw-Hill

Name _____

As you read *Wild Horses*, fill in the Cause and Effect Diagram.

Cause	➡	Effect
	➡	
	➡	
	➡	
	➡	

How does the information you wrote in the Cause and Effect Diagram help you to monitor your comprehension of *Wild Horses*?

At Home: Have the student use the chart to retell the story.

Wild Horses
Grade 4/Unit 5

179

As I read, I will pay attention to the pronunciation of vocabulary words.

	Once there were millions of buffalo. The buffalo lived on the
11	Great Plains. Buffalo were a main source of food for the Native
23	Americans of the Plains. Hunting buffalo was an important part of life.
35	Hunting was hard. Hunters had to walk everywhere. It was hard to
47	surprise the buffalo. Buffalo have a good sense of smell. If they smell
60	danger, they run.
63	But there was a way to fool the buffalo. The hunters covered
75	themselves with wolf skins. Then the buffalo did not smell the hunters.
87	They did not feel threatened so they did not run away.
98	The hunters crept close to the buffalo. When they were very close,
110	they killed the buffalo with arrows and spears.
118	Once horses were brought to the Plains things changed. Horses
128	meant that the tribes of the Plains could hunt over greater distances.
140	On horseback, hunters could move quickly. 146

Comprehension Check

1. What changed the lives of Plains Indians? What was the effect of that change? **Cause and Effect**

2. How did people hunt buffalo before horses? **Summarize**

	Words Read	–	Number of Errors	=	Words Correct Score
First Read		–		=	
Second Read		–		=	

© Macmillan/McGraw-Hill

At Home: Help the student read the passage, paying attention to the goal at the top of the page.

A **figure of speech** is an unusual or creative way to use words. One kind of figure of speech is **hyperbole.** This is the use of exaggeration to make a point about something or to make things seem more dramatic. The writer doesn't expect readers to really believe the exaggeration.

Underline the words in the sentences below that are examples of hyperbole.

1. My uncle's ranch is so big that he'll never get to see all of it during his lifetime.

2. When ranch hands are sent out to mend the fences, they don't come back for years!

3. The best part of summers at the ranch is Lightning.

4. I just saddle up that stallion and tap my heels against his sides, and he takes off like a shot.

5. One day Lightning and I were moving so fast my uncle wondered how a freight train got onto his land.

6. This year my uncle said I was old enough to help with the round-up.

7. Uncle Bob woke me up before the sun had come up and we went downstairs for flapjacks, fresh eggs, and sausages.

8. I was so hungry I could have eaten a horse.

9. Auntie Mae's flapjacks were lighter than air, so you could eat a ton of them before you felt full.

10. Suddenly I realized everyone had stopped eating to watch me fill my plate, and I thought my uncle would die laughing!

 At Home: Together with the student, use hyperbole, or exaggeration, to describe items in your home.

Name _____

When you read, you might come across a word that you do not know. Sometimes, the other words and sentences in the paragraph can give you **context clues** to help you figure out the word's meaning.

I heard a <u>whinnying</u> *right next to me. I jumped in surprise. There, sticking its head through my window, was our neighbor's horse! It snorted and shook its head.*

If the word *whinnying* is unfamiliar to you, you can figure out its meaning by reading the rest of the paragraph. The description in the surrounding text helps you understand that *whinnying* must be the sound a horse makes.

A. Read the passage below. As you read, use context clues to figure out the meanings of the words in dark print. Underline the context clues you found.

    The ground **trembled** under my feet. The horse **herd** was huge. There must have been more than a hundred horses in the group. I could not tell what started the **stampede** but something had spooked those horses. As they galloped by, the noise was much louder than I had imagined it would be. Their hoofbeats **echoed** off the rock walls of the canyon.

B. Circle the best definition of each word.

1. trembled
   a. broke   **b.** shook   **c.** sunk

2. herd
   a. sound   **b.** group of horses   **c.** color

3. stampede
   a. the sudden flight of   **b.** round-up   **c.** competition of
       frightened animals   trained ponies

4. echoed
   a. repeated the sound of   **b.** were getting quieter   **c.** crumbled

At Home: Together with the student, discuss which context clues helped him or her determine the meanings of the above words.

The /əl/ sound is what you hear at the end of the word *level*.
There are several letter pairs that can stand for this sound.
- **al** as in *pedal*
- **el** as in *level*
- **il** as in *pencil*
- **le** as in *turtle*

In a dictionary pronunciation, this sound is usually spelled *əl*.

A. Read each sentence. Circle the word that has the /əl/ sound.

1. We hoped to spot wild horses on our drive, but didn't see a single one.

2. Although the numbers are growing, the total number of wild horses is unknown.

3. Many think of the American mustang as the jewel of the western wilderness.

4. Pupils learning about conservation of the western range volunteer their time at the ranch.

5. It is not easy to care for a horse with an injured ankle.

B. Circle the words in each row that have the final /əl/ sound.

6. only	tunnel	mammal	animal
7. postal	vacation	total	tickle
8. pasted	elder	settle	brittle
9. model	sensor	fasten	paddle
10. shovel	piston	well	awhile
11. tonsil	circle	final	pickle
12. bucket	Elton	kettle	female

At Home: Together, identify the different /əl/ spellings in the words circled above. Then try to think of other words with the /əl/ sound.

© Macmillan/McGraw-Hill

A. Write a word from the box to complete each sentence.

positive	specialty	cranky	estimated	swarms

1. My little brother Tim gets _____ if he doesn't take a nap.

2. _____ of people came to the art show.

3. I was _____ that I would win the spelling bee.

4. We _____ that the boat trip would take three hours.

5. My Dad loves to cook. His _____ is French toast.

B. Match each vocabulary word to its synonym.

6. vessels   **a.** a safe place

7. peculiar   **b.** ships

8. glorious   **c.** wonderful

9. sanctuary   **d.** sparkling

10. glistening   **e.** odd

C. Read each question. Choose a vocabulary word from the box to answer the question. Write your answer on the line.

fragile	collage	valuable	bumbling	snuffled

11. How did you breathe when you had a cold? I _____.

12. Which word describes something that is worth a lot of money?

_____

13. How can you describe something that can be easily broken?

_____

14. If you saw a man knock over many things in a store, how might you

describe him? _____

15. If you put together a picture made of the scraps of other pictures, what

did you make? _____

D. Supply words from the box to complete the paragraph.

barbecue	flicked	threatened	famished	consisted

    Yesterday, my friends came over to play. After swimming

in the pool, we were **16.** _____ and ready to eat. We

had a **17.** _____. Dad put together a great meal. It

18. _____ of hamburgers, hotdogs, salad, and baked beans.

Soon, dark clouds **19.** _____ to end the fun. So we went in,

20. _____ on the lights, and continued our fun indoors.

Name _____

annoyed	prospectors	outstretched	circular
glinted	reference	disappointment	

Write a word from the vocabulary list to complete each sentence.

1. _____ were not always successful in their hunt for gold.

2. Many gold seekers felt _____ because they found very little of it.

3. To pan for gold, you have to swirl a pan of river water in a

   _____ motion.

4. The old miner shook my _____ hand when we met.

5. When John Marshall first found gold, his eye was drawn to a rock that

   _____ in the sunlight.

6. When I wrote my report on the gold rush, I used encyclopedias for

   _____.

7. I felt _____ that I didn't live back then. I would have loved to pan for gold.

Write a sentence that includes three of the vocabulary words.

8. _____

   _____

   _____

An **effect** is what happens. A **cause** it why it happens.

The girls got soaked because they forgot their umbrellas.

Ask yourself, "What happened?" The answer, "The girls got soaked," is the **effect**. Ask "Why did it happen?" The answer, "The girls forgot their umbrellas," is the **cause**.

Read each passage. Then circle the correct answer.

Many of the people who headed west in 1849 did not bring enough water. Some ran out of water in the Nevada desert. Clever men brought barrels of water from California to Nevada. They charged thirsty travelers as much as $100 for a glass of water.

1. What was the effect of travelers not having enough water?
   a. They had to pay a lot of money for water.
   b. They turned back and did not reach California.
   c. They went to California with barrels of water.

2. What caused people to pay $100 for a glass of water?
   a. They thought it tasted great.
   b. They needed water to survive.
   c. They liked the men who were selling it.

Two California gold miners got fed up with mining. They sold their mining cabin to three men for $25. The new owners took the cabin apart. In the spaces between the floorboards, they gathered gold dust that had fallen off the men's clothing. The gold dust was worth $300!

3. What caused the two miners to sell their cabin?
   a. They had gold dust on their clothes.
   b. They wanted to run off and search for gold.
   c. They got fed up with gold mining.

4. What effect did taking the cabin apart have for the new owners?
   a. The cabin wasn't good for anything.
   b. The new owners made a lot of money.
   c. The gold miners gave up on mining.

© Macmillan/McGraw-Hill

At Home: Discuss something that happened in school. Together, identify what caused the event to happen.

The Gold Rush Game
Grade 4/Unit 6

187

Name _____

As you read *The Gold Rush Game*, fill in the Cause and Effect Diagram.

Cause ⟶	Effect
⟶	
⟶	
⟶	
⟶	

How does the information you wrote in the Cause and Effect Diagram help you to analyze the story structure of *The Gold Rush Game*?

 At Home: Have the student use the chart to retell the story.

As I read, I will pay attention to pauses, stops, and intonation.

	Gold is a shiny metal. It is rare and hard to find. It has
14	been a valuable metal since ancient times. People pay
23	a lot of money for it. A few ounces of gold are worth
36	hundreds of dollars. People will travel a long way and
46	risk danger in search of it. When someone does find
56	gold, the news spreads quickly.
61	As the United States grew, people went west, where
70	they discovered new things. Some found good farmland.
78	Others found a place for raising cattle. A few found gold.
89	This was always the most exciting news.
96	The years from 1848 to 1900 were a time of great
105	gold rushes in the United States. Thousands of people
114	hoped to strike it rich. California's gold rush is the most
125	famous. But there were others. Gold was discovered
133	in Georgia. There was a rush for gold in Colorado. 143

Comprehension Check

1. What happened when gold was discovered? **Cause and Effect**

2. In history, how has the discovery of gold affected people? **Plot and Character**

	Words Read	–	Number of Errors	=	Words Correct Score
First Read		–		=	
Second Read		–		=	

At Home: Help the student read the passage, paying attention to the goal at the top of the page.

The Gold Rush Game
Grade 4/Unit 6

189

A **timeline** helps you picture a sequence of events that happened in the past.

Read the timeline and answer the questions that follow.

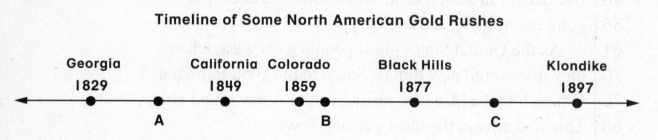

Timeline of Some North American Gold Rushes

| Georgia | California | Colorado | Black Hills | Klondike |
| 1829 | 1849 | 1859 | 1877 | 1897 |

A   B   C

1. In what year did the earliest gold rush shown on the timeline happen?

   a. 1829

   b. 1849

   c. 1859

2. What gold rush happened in 1877?

   a. California

   b. Colorado

   c. Black Hills

3. In what year did the Klondike Gold Rush occur?

   a. 1829

   b. 1859

   c. 1897

4. If you wanted to add an event that happened in 1839, where would you place it on the timeline?

   a. point A

   b. point B

   c. point C

© Macmillan/McGraw-Hill

At Home: Have the student make a timeline of events in his or her life during the past week. Have him or her draw a line, make seven even markings, and write an event for each day.

Name _____

A **suffix** is a word ending that changes the meaning of the word.
When added to a verb, the suffixes *-er* and *-or* mean
"a person who."

   build + er = builder   *sail + or = sailor*

A build**er** is "a person who builds." A sail**or** is "a person who sails."

**Add the suffix *-er* or *-or* to each word and write the meaning
of the new word in Part A. Then use the words you made to
complete the sentences in Part B.**

Part A.

 1. work + er = _____ _____

 2. play + er = _____ _____

 3. collect + or = _____ _____

 4. visit + or = _____ _____

 5. sail + or = _____ _____

Part B.

 6. You would have to be a hard _____ to prospect for gold.

 7. My grandfather was a _____ of old photos from the
  mining camps.

 8. A _____ on one of the big 19th-century sailing ships had
  to work hard.

 9. Would you like to be a Gold Rush game _____?

 10. It would be fun to be a _____ to another time and place.

At Home: Discuss what the following words mean: *writer,
reader, dishwasher, manager, editor.*

The Gold Rush Game
Grade 4/Unit 6

Name _____

You can hear the same ending sounds in the words *cannon* and *golden*. It is the **/ən/** sound. The sound can be spelled *-en, -in,* or *-on.*

A. Find and circle each word from the box. Then write the word on the line.

eaten   sunken   season   open   bacon   cousin   reason   often

1. a v l o f t e n h o t _____

2. f e g w a c o u s i n _____

3. t y r e a s o n p o n _____

4. n m q e a t e n u n e _____

5. s p o p e n j e o n k _____

6. a s u n k e n c i x y _____

7. b a c o n w u n v o n _____

8. l d f s e a s o n o _____

B. Circle the word that ends with the /ən/ sound.

9. green   eleven   sailor

10. raisin   raising   rain

11. between   using   button

12. along   muffin   train

 At Home: Take turns spelling the words on this page.

Name _____

| wistfully | eavesdropping | scuffling | jumble |
| acquaintance | scornfully | logical | |

A. Find and circle the vocabulary word that matches each meaning.

Meanings	**Words**
1. wishfully and sadly	t y u g n a w i s t f u l l y i f w
2. listening in secret	d v e e a v e s d r o p p i n g h e
3. scraping or dragging	n s c u f f l i n g q i h u c e g a
4. a big mess	n u m p x e j u m b l e r i s z u f
5. someone you know a little	s a c q u a i n t a n c e c v b a i l
6. with dislike and disrespect	f y s o r t s c o r n f u l l y s y o
7. reasonable, making sense	i l o g i c a l c b h u t r a v i m l e t

B. Select three vocabulary words and use each in a sentence of your own.

8. _____

9. _____

10. _____

A **theme** is what a story is about. The author usually doesn't tell readers what the theme is. Readers have to figure it out from what the characters say and do. To find the theme, ask yourself, "What is the story about?"

Read the passage. As you read, think about the story's theme. Then circle the correct answer.

Felicia liked her hideaway in the back of the garden. It had once been a shed and had a good roof and glass in the windows. She loved sitting in the chair she had brought in, reading. Every evening after supper Felicia would sing a little song she had made up about her house. But as much as she loved the house, Felicia was lonely. She played all alone in the house and wished she had some friends. "Just one good friend would make me as happy as can be!" she said. "Then my life would be full."

1. The theme of this story is

   a. houses

   b. wanting friends

   c. singing songs

2. Which of these is a clue to the story's theme?

   a. Felicia is lonely.

   b. Felicia likes to read.

   c. Felicia's hideaway is in the back of the garden.

3. Which of these events would you add to the story to fit in with the theme?

   a. Felicia falls asleep in the house.

   b. Felicia goes looking for a friend.

   c. Felicia gets a ride on a bird's back.

4. What might Felicia see in another garden that would make her want to visit?

   _____

   _____

At Home: Discuss one of the student's favorite stories. Together, see if you can identify the story's theme.

As you read *The Cricket in Times Square*, fill in the Theme Map.

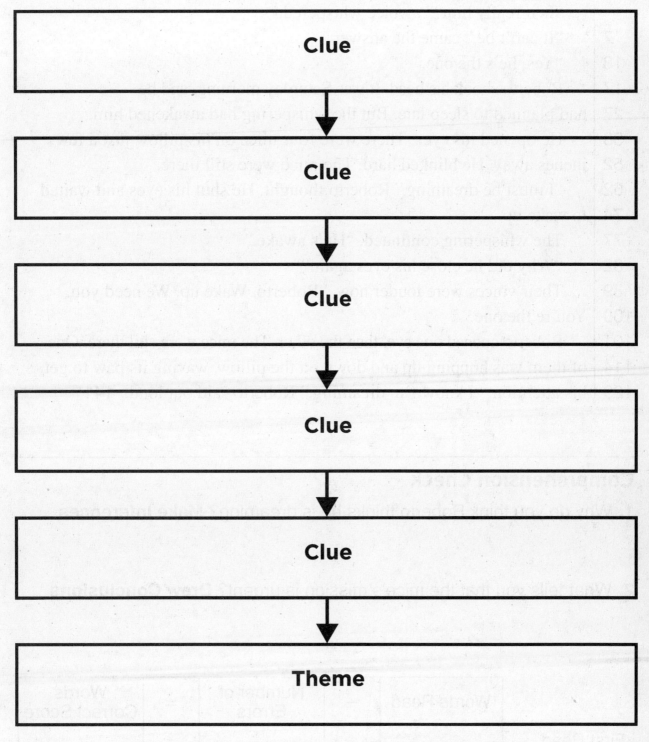

Clue

↓

Clue

↓

Clue

↓

Clue

↓

Clue

↓

Theme

How does the information you wrote in the Theme Map help you to analyze the story structure of *The Cricket in Times Square*?

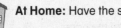 **At Home:** Have the student use the chart to retell the story.

As I read, I will pay attention to punctuation in each sentence.

	"Is it really him?" a voice whispered.
7	"It can't be," came the answer.
13	"Yes, he's the one."
17	Roberto shook his head. It was Saturday morning, and he
27	had planned to sleep late. But the whispering had awakened him.
38	He opened his eyes. There were four mice on his pillow just a few
52	inches away. He blinked hard. The mice were still there.
62	"I must be dreaming," Roberto thought. He shut his eyes and waited
74	to wake up.
77	The whispering continued. "He's awake."
82	"Why did he close his eyes again?"
89	Their voices were louder now. "Roberto. Wake up. We need you.
100	You're the one."
101	Roberto opened one eye, then the other. The mice were still there. One
114	of them was hopping up and down on the pillow, waving its paw to get
129	his attention. "I know I'm dreaming," Roberto said out loud. 141

Comprehension Check

1. Why do you think Roberto thinks he is dreaming? **Make Inferences**

2. What tells you that the mice's mission is urgent? **Draw Conclusions**

	Words Read	−	Number of Errors	=	Words Correct Score
First Read		−		=	
Second Read		−		=	

196 The Cricket in Times Square
Grade 4/Unit 6

At Home: Help the student read the passage, paying attention to the goal at the top of the page.

An **advertisement** usually tries to get people to buy something. Advertisers use different **techniques** to convince people to buy their product:

- using words that make a product look good or sound important
- telling people to buy or do something because everyone else is
- saying that their product is the least expensive or the best deal

Read the advertisement and answer the questions that follow.

Walk with the Crowd!

Show a child that you love him. Purchase one of these adorable stuffed monkeys. At the same time, your purchase will raise money for the Save the Monkey fund. Bring a smile to a child's face and help a beautiful animal. Call today—these adorable toys will be gone soon.

Call (555) 987–6543 to order your stuffed animal.

1. According to the ad, people who purchase a stuffed monkey will
a. make a child happy and save a monkey.
b. save a lot of money.

2. According to the advertisement, what will happen if people don't order today?
a. Real monkeys will disappear.
b. There will be no more stuffed monkeys left.

At Home: Together, discuss advertisements that you see in magazines, newspapers, or on TV.

The Cricket in Times Square
Grade 4/Unit 6

When you read, you may come across a word that you do not know. Sometimes, other sentences in the paragraph can give you **context clues** to help you figure out what the word means.

Circle the letter that best matches the meaning of the word in bold. Underline the context clues that help you figure out the word's meaning.

1. The squirrel was **munching** on a nut. He held it between his paws as he chewed it noisily.

   a. hiding

   b. eating

   c. holding something tightly

2. Gregory Groundhog **peered** anxiously around the yard, trying to locate who or what had made the frightening sound.

   a. jumped

   b. sounded

   c. searched

3. The carpenter pulled the boards apart. They **separated** rather easily.

   a. moved apart

   b. came together

   c. broke

4. Michael Mouse was good at **scrounging** for food. He sniffed along the floor, finding the tiniest bits of cheese and bread crumbs.

   a. gathering with difficulty

   b. throwing away

   c. stuffing into one's mouth

5. The fire was **blazing.** Bright red flames danced high into the night sky.

   a. burning brightly

   b. almost out

   c. cool

6. We could see clear **azure** skies over us. Their bright blue color was reflected in the lake below.

   a. cloudy

   b. blue

   c. below

© Macmillan/McGraw-Hill

 At Home: Together, read a paragraph. Use context clues to identify the meanings of words the student does not know.

Name _____

Say these words: *tail, tale.*
Some words sound the same, but have different spellings
and meanings. These words are called **homophones**.
The words *hour* and *our* are homophones.
        hour = 60 minutes   our = belonging to us

**For each set of words, cross out the word that is not a
homophone.**

1. prince   pinch   prints

2. meant   meet   meat

3. too   two   tow

4. seed   sea   see

5. pear   par   pair

6. not   knot   note

7. war   wear   where

8. made   maid   mad

9. wade   wait   weighed

10. rot   root   route

11. done   doe   dough

12. patients   patience   pencils

© Macmillan/McGraw-Hill

At Home: With the student, name as many other pairs of
homophones as you can.

| fossil | paleontologist | inspected | stumbled upon |

Read each question. Write the vocabulary word that answers it. Then fill in the puzzle.

1. What did the scientist do when she looked at something carefully?

_____

2. What is the name for a scientist who studies fossils?

_____

3. What is the name for a preserved part of an animal that lived long ago?

_____

4. If you found something by accident, what did you do?

_____ it

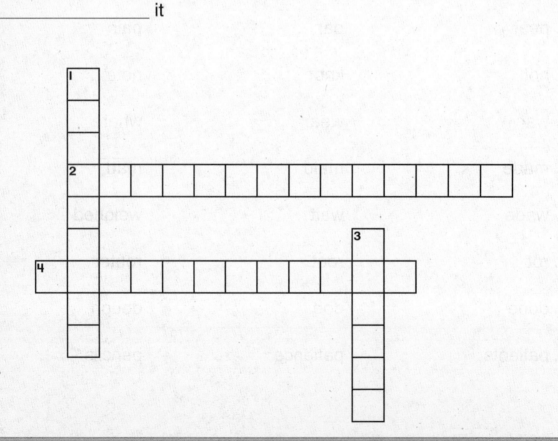

© Macmillan/McGraw-Hill

> A **generalization** is a broad statement about many people, many animals, or many things. A generalization can be true or not true. For example:
>
> Most animals have legs. TRUE
>
> All animals have legs. NOT TRUE (Snakes don't have legs.)

Read each set of facts below and apply the information you already know. Then circle the generalization you can make about the facts.

1. Deer grow antlers. Elk grow antlers. Moose grow antlers.

   a. All animals grow antlers.   **b.** Some animals grow antlers.

2. Parrots can be taught to speak. Myna birds can, too. So can parakeets.

   a. Birds can speak.   **b.** Some birds can speak.

3. Scientists have found a scorpion fossil in amber. They've also found fossils of flowers and ants.

   a. Amber is a good place to look   **b.** You can find any kind of fossil
      for fossils.   you want in amber.

4. Gorillas can make several different sounds to "talk" to each other. They work very hard to protect their young. Gorillas can be taught sign language.

   a. Gorillas can do many things.   **b.** Gorillas can do anything.

5. Chuckwalla lizards can survive in areas with little water. Chuckawallas are plant-eaters. Chuckwallas hide among the rocks when threatened.

   a. Chuckwallas are fierce reptiles.   **b.** Chuckwallas are not
                                                   aggressive animals.

© Macmillan/McGraw-Hill

At Home: Together, talk about the weather in your area over the past few months. Ask the student to make generalizations to describe it.

Meet a Bone-ified Explorer
Grade 4/Unit 6

Name _____

As you read *Meet a Bone-ified Explorer,* fill in the
Generalizations Chart.

Information from Text	What I Know	Generalization

How does the information you wrote in this Generalizations Chart
help you analyze the text structure of *Meet a Bone-ified Explorer*?

At Home: Have the student use the chart to retell the story.

Name _____

As I read, I will pay attention to the pronunciation of vocabulary and other difficult words.

	Pompeii was buried under eight to ten feet of ash and
11	rock. Only the tops of some buildings could be seen.
21	People who had escaped came back to search through the
31	rubble and find their homes.
36	Over time, people stopped searching for their homes.
44	Pompeii became a forgotten city, lost in ash and rock.
54	Hundreds of years passed. The whole city of Pompeii
63	was now covered with debris. People never guessed that
72	a lost city was buried near the smoking volcano.
81	In 1710, a well digger **stumbled upon** the remains of
90	a building in a nearby town. Soon people began to realize
101	that this was the ancient city of Pompeii. Explorers and
111	scientists began to dig up the lost city. As they **inspected**
122	the ruins, they found vases, statues, and parts of homes. 132

Comprehension Check

1. Why were people interested in Pompeii? **Make Generalizations**

2. How was Pompeii found again? **Cause and Effect**

	Words Read	–	Number of Errors	=	Words Correct Score
First Read		–		=	
Second Read		–		=	

© Macmillan/McGraw-Hill

At Home: Help the student read the passage, paying attention to the goal at the top of the page.

A **functional document** is a piece of writing that helps you to do something. Recipes, forms, and invitations are functional documents.
A **recipe** tells you how to cook something.
A **form** collects and organizes facts.
An **invitation** gives you information about an event.

Please come to a birthday party!

When: January 10th at 4:00 pm

Where: 3648 Acorn Avenue

Call 555-3181 to tell us whether you can make it.

Please bring gifts for the city animal shelter only, please.

Circle the answer to each question.

1. What kind of functional document is in the box?

   a. a recipe   **b.** an invitation

2. What is the date of the party?

   a. January 10th   **b.** January 4th

3. Where will the party be held?

   a. the animal shelter   **b.** 3648 Acorn Avenue.

4. How will you let them know if you can come?

   a. Call 555-3181.   **b.** The invitation does not say.

At Home: Together, create an invitation for a real or imaginary event.

Name _____

A root is a word part that is used to form many words. If you know the meaning of a root, you can figure out the meaning of unfamiliar words.

Words that have the root *aud* have to do with hearing.

Words that have the root *spec* have to do with seeing.

Read each word below. Then circle the meaning that best fits it, based on the information above.

1. audio

   a. the pictures in a movie   **b.** the words and sounds for a movie

2. inspector

   a. someone who looks at   **b.** someone who
   things closely   listens to things closely

3. spectacles

   a. glasses to help you see   **b.** hearing aids to help you hear

4. spectacular

   a. amazing to hear   **b.** amazing to see

5. audible

   a. able to be seen   **b.** able to be heard

6. spectator

   a. someone who watches   **b.** someone who listens in
   an event

© Macmillan/McGraw-Hill

At Home: Take turns using each word above in a sentence.

A prefix is a word part that can be added to the beginning of a base word and that changes its meaning. The prefixes *dis-*, *non-*, and *un-* mean "the opposite of" or "without." The prefix *mis-* means "badly" or "incorrectly."

disrespect = without respect   *unhappy* = opposite of happy
nonstop = without a stop   *misbehave* = behave badly

Answer each question with a word from the box that has the same meaning as the underlined words.

uncovered	disappeared	unbelievable
nonfiction	misjudge	disagree

1. What is the most <u>the opposite of believable</u> thing someone has told

   you about dinosaurs? _____

2. What should you do if you <u>do not agree</u> with something you have read?

   _____

3. What kind of <u>not fiction book</u> do you like to read? _____

4. What would you do if you <u>opposite of covered</u> a fossil in your yard?

   _____

5. Why do you think the dinosaurs <u>opposite of appeared</u>?

   _____

6. What might happen if you <u>incorrectly judge</u> your location?

   _____

© Macmillan/McGraw-Hill

At Home: With the student, add the prefixes above to other words to create four new words.

Name _____

| assured | glider | unstable | hoisting |
| headlines | applauded | wingspan | |

A. Write a word from the box to complete each sentence.

1. A _____ is a light aircraft that flies using air currents.

2. A bicycle tips easily without a rider because it is _____.

3. When something is certain, it is _____.

4. People cheered and _____ the first flight.

5. The distance between the tips of a plane's or bird's wings is its

   _____.

6. Newspaper _____ announced the first flight at Kitty Hawk.

7. On the day of their first flight, Will and Orv were seen

   _____ a red flag to the top of a pole.

B. Write three sentences, each using one of the vocabulary words.

8. _____
   _____

9. _____
   _____

10. _____
    _____

> An **author's perspective** is the author's thoughts and feelings about his or her subject. The author does not usually come out and say, "This is my perspective." Instead, readers have to pay attention to what the author has written.

Read each passage. Then circle the correct answers to the questions that follow.

Have you ever flown in an airplane? It's incredible! The plane revs its engines and starts down the runway. In no time at all, you are in the air. If you get a window seat, you can look outside. You might see fluffy clouds. Or if it's clear, you can look down at the landscape. If you look closely, you might even see something you recognize!

1. How does the author feel about flying?

a. The author thinks it's wonderful.

b. The author thinks it's unsafe.

2. Which statement shows how the author feels about flying?

a. The plane revs its engines

b. It's incredible!

Have you ever tried to build model airplanes? I like to build models with lots of parts. I try to make each plane just like the original. When I finish a plane, I hang it in my room. I have a whole sky full! Building model airplanes is fun and educational. You should try it!

3. How does the author feel about building model airplanes?

a. He thinks it's a boring hobby.

b. He thinks it's a great hobby.

4. Which sentence(s) gives a clue to the author's feelings?

a. Building model airplanes is fun and educational. You should try it!

b. Have you ever tried to build model airplanes?

© Macmillan/McGraw-Hill

At Home: With the student, rewrite one of the passages above to express a different perspective.

Name _____

As you read *My Brother's Flying Machine*, fill in the Author's Perspective Map.

Clue	Clue	Clue

Author's Perspective

How does the information you wrote in the Author's Perspective Map help you to monitor your comprehension of *My Brothers' Flying Machine*?

At Home: Have the student use the chart to retell the story.

My Brothers' Flying Machine
Grade 4/Unit 6

© Macmillan/McGraw-Hill

Name _____

As I read, I will pay attention to tempo in order to match the action in the story.

	In the early 1900s, airplanes were new. Experiments in
8	flight had been going on for about 100 years. But flight
18	still had a long way to go.
25	In 1902, the Wright brothers built a **glider**. Then
33	they built an engine-powered plane. In 1903 that plane
41	made its first flight. Soon people began to dream of flying
52	where no one had flown before.
58	Of course the Wright Brothers were men. So were
67	most of the other early flyers. Women were not expected
77	to become pilots. Women were expected to stay home as
87	wives and mothers. Women who did work outside the
96	home were usually not paid the same as men for equal
107	work. Women could not even vote.
113	Some women dreamed of doing things others thought
121	they should not do. One of these women was Amelia
131	Earhart. She wanted to be a pilot. She didn't think the sky
143	belonged only to men. 147

Comprehension Check

1. Why do you think the author states that flight still had a long way to go? **Make Inferences**

2. What opinion did Amelia Earhart hold about flying? **Fact and Opinion**

	Words Read	–	Number of Errors	=	Words Correct Score
First Read		–		=	
Second Read		–		=	

My Brothers' Flying Machine
Grade 4/Unit 6

At Home: Help the student read the passage, paying attention to the goal at the top of the page.

Name _____

Poets have different ways to make their poems more interesting or powerful.

Repetition is when a poet uses a word or phrase more than once in a poem.

Personification is when an animal, thing, or idea acts like or is described as if it were a person.

The toy airplane squirmed with excitement when the boy looked at it.

Read each poem. Circle the correct answers to the questions that follow.

> The rabbit cried out,
> "Don't make me go!
> I really hate flying.
> Please let me say NO."

1. What is an example of personification in this poem?

   a. A person is telling the story.   **b.** The rabbit talks.

> I love to fly,
> Go way up high.
> When I come down,
> I wear a frown.
>
> I love to fly.
> I say good-bye.
> And when I land,
> I'll wave my hand!

2. Which words are an example of repetition?

   a. I love to fly.   **b.** I say goodbye.

© Macmillan/McGraw-Hill

At Home: Read poems with the student. Look for examples of personification and repetition.

To change many verbs to the past tense, add the ending *-ed*.
Use past-tense verbs to tell about something that has already
happened.
PRESENT TENSE: We **watch** the plane take off.
PAST TENSE: Yesterday, we **watched** the plane take off.

**A. Circle the past-tense verb in each sentence. Then write it
on the line.**

1. The plane climbed high in the sky. _____

2. It soared higher and higher. _____

3. The pilot winked at us from the cockpit. _____

4. We screamed in order to hear each other over the noise of the engines.

   _____

5. We talked about becoming pilots some day. _____

B. Write the past-tense form of each verb.

6. row _____

7. sprint _____

8. fix _____

9. turn _____

10. pitch _____

© Macmillan/McGraw-Hill

At Home: With the student, take turns naming as many
verbs with the *-ed* ending as you can.

Name _____

A **suffix** is a word part that can be added to the end of a base word. Adding a suffix changes the meaning of the base word.

y and *-ful* mean "full of"   rain + y = rainy   help + ful = helpful
-ly means "in a certain way"   careful + ly = carefully
-less means "without"   pain + less = painless
-ness means "the state of being"   kind + ness = kindness

Read each sentence. Circle the word that has the same meaning as the underlined words.

1. Amelia Earhart flew a plane <u>in a brave way</u>.

   a. braveness   b. bravely   c. braveful

2. Orv and Will were <u>full of joy</u> when their plane flew.

   a. joyful   b. joyness   c. joyless

3. The plane felt <u>without weight</u> when it was up in the sky.

   a. weighty   b. weightly   c. weightless

4. Is is a good idea to fly on a <u>full of clouds</u> day?

   a. cloudful   b. cloudy   c. cloudly

5. The first flight was a <u>full of wonder</u> sight.

   a. wonderness   b. wonderly   c. wonderful

6. Orv and Will were filled with <u>the state of being glad</u>.

   a. gladly   b. gladful   c. gladness

7. Orv and Will carried on <u>in a sad way</u> after their mother died.

   a. sadly   b. sadless   c. sadful

8. Modern airplanes are <u>full of speed</u> compared to the first ones.

   a. speedless   b. speedy   c. speedly

At Home: Take turns making up sentences that include the words above.

My Brothers' Flying Machine
Grade 4/Unit 6

213

Name _____

astronomer	investigates	solitary	territory
communication	nutrients	prehistoric	overcome

A. Read each clue. Then write the correct word from the box.

1. This word describes things such as talking and writing.

   _____

2. This word describes you when you're alone. _____

3. This word means "be victorious over." _____

4. This word describes a period of time. _____

5. This word names healthy things found in food. _____

6. This word names someone who studies the stars and planets.

   _____

7. This is another word for an area of land. _____

8. This word is what a detective does. _____

B. Write two sentences, each using one word from the box.

9. _____

   _____

10. _____

   _____

Writers use **description** to help readers better understand
something. Description also makes reading more interesting by
including details that tell about how something looks, smells,
feels, tastes, or sounds.

Read the passage. Then answer the questions that follow.

What Ants Eat

Most ants eat whatever they can find. But some ants are fussy.

Harvester ants gather and store grains or grass seed. Some kinds
of harvester ants have an even more specialized job. Their only job is
to crack open seeds so that other ants can eat them.

Other ants eat fungus that they grow in their nest. Some of these
ants cut leaves and bring them back to the nest. The leaves help the
fungus grow.

Some ants like a sweet drink called *honeydew*. Aphids, another insect,
make the honeydew. The job of certain ants is to fill their bodies with
honeydew. Then they feed the other ants.

1. What was this text structured to describe?

   a. ants   **b.** what ants eat

2. Are most ants fussy eaters?

   a. Yes, they eat only one thing.   **b.** No, most ants eat whatever
                                    they can find.

3. What do the ants use to grow fungus?

   a. cut leaves   **b.** grains and seeds

4. Which detail in the selection relates to our sense of taste?

   a. Some ants like a sweet   **b.** Harvester ants have a
      drink called *honeydew.*   more specialized job.

© Macmillan/McGraw-Hill

At Home: Ask the student to use sensory details to describe
a person, place, or thing.

The Life and Times of the Ant
Grade 4/Unit 6

215

**As you read _The Life and Times of the Ant_, fill in the
Description Web.**

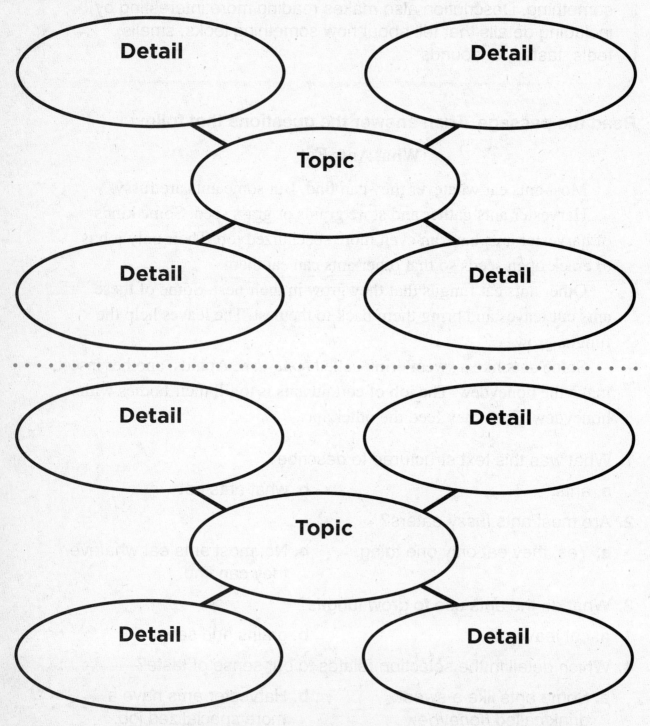

How does completing the Description Web help you analyze the text
structure of _The Life and Times of the Ant_?

 At Home: Have the student use the chart to retell the story.

© Macmillan/McGraw-Hill

Name _____

As I read, I will pay attention to the pronunciation of vocabulary words.

	You may know that some birds fly south in the winter.
11	Many butterflies and moths do too, but only one kind
21	of butterfly truly migrates. Monarch butterflies fly south
29	when it gets cold in the North. They return to where they
41	started later in the year. These butterflies can cover 1,000
50	miles (1,609 km) in a few days. In all, the trip can be more
63	than 4,000 miles (6,437 km) long.
67	But that's not the only interesting thing about their
76	journey. Monarch butterfly eggs hatch in the South during
85	the warm winter months. The caterpillars grow into adult
94	butterflies. It is these new monarch butterflies that make
103	the trip back north. These butterflies know exactly where
112	to go and when to fly even though they have never made
124	the trip before. They visit the same **territory** as the
134	butterflies that went before them. 139

Comprehension Check

1. Describe what butterflies that hatch in the South can do. **Description**

2. Summarize what the monarch butterfly does. **Summarize**

	Words Read	–	Number of Errors	=	Words Correct Score
First Read		–		=	
Second Read		–		=	

At Home: Help the student read the passage, paying attention to the goal at the top of the page.

The Life and Times of the Ant
Grade 4/Unit 6

217

Name _____

A **fable** is a short story that usually has animal characters.
The **plot** is what happens to the characters in the story.
The **moral** is the lesson that we learn from the fable.

Read the fable. Then answer the questions that follow.

A lion was asleep when a mouse ran across his face. The lion woke up angry. He decided to eat the mouse. The mouse begged him not to. He said that he would repay the kindness someday. The lion laughed. He didn't think a small animal could ever help a big lion. But he let the mouse go.

One day, some hunters caught the lion and tied him up with ropes. The mouse heard the lion roar. He knew the lion needed help. The mouse found the lion and chewed through the ropes that held him. The lion got away. He was surprised that a small animal could help him after all.

1. Number these story events from 1–5 in the correct order to make a summary of the story's plot.

____ The lion decided to eat the mouse.

____ The mouse chewed through the ropes.

____ The lion let the mouse go.

____ A mouse ran across a lion's face.

____ Hunters caught the lion.

2. What is the moral of this story?

    a. You don't have to be big to help.   **b.** Mice should stay away from lions.

 At Home: Discuss the plots and morals of other fables you know with the student.

A **root** is a word part that is used to form many words. Many English words have roots that come from the Greek language. Knowing the meanings of these roots can help you figure out unfamiliar words.

bio- = life   -logy = the study of   biology = the study of life

Greek Root	Meaning
astro-	star
geo-	Earth
bio-	life
-logy	the study of
-graph	write

Use the Greek roots and their meanings to answer the following questions.

1. What do *astronomers* study?

   a. stars   **b.** the earth

2. What is the meaning of *geology*?

   a. Earth star   **b.** the study of Earth

3. Which kind of scientist is more likely to study ants?

   a. an astronomer   **b.** a biologist

4. Which word describes writing that tells about someone's life?

   a. biography   **b.** geography

5. Use one of the Greek root words above in a sentence.

   _____

   _____

© Macmillan/McGraw-Hill

At Home: Use the meanings of the Greek roots above to discuss the meaning of the word *geography*.

The Life and Times of the Ant
Grade 4/Unit 6

219

A **stressed syllable** is the part of the word that gets added weight when you say it. Syllables with *er* can be either stressed or unstressed.
- Stressed syllable: service   **ser** / *vice* (sûr´ vis)
- Unstressed syllable: lantern   **lan** / *tern* (lan´ tərn)

When *er* is in a stressed syllable, it has the /ûr/ sound.
The sound can be spelled three ways:
- *er* as in *service*
- *ir* as in *dirty*
- *ur* as in *purple*

Circle the stressed syllable in each of the following words. Then write the letters that stand for the /ûr/ sound.

1. circle   cir / cle _____

2. return   re / turn _____

3. thirty   thir / ty _____

4. burrow   bur / row _____

5. curtain   cur / tain _____

6. certain   cer / tain _____

7. service   ser / vice _____

8. whirlwind   whirl / wind _____

9. furnace   fur / nace _____

10. disturb   dis / turb _____

At Home: Take turns with the student spelling the words on this page.

© Macmillan/McGraw-Hill

Name _____

A. Write a word from the box to complete each sentence.

| circular | inspected | applauded | solitary | territory |

1. The class _____ at the end of my presentation on ant families.

2. James dug up a _____ object in his backyard.

3. Do ants live _____ lives, or do they live in groups?

4. The scientist _____ the insect with a magnifying glass and carefully counted its legs.

5. Jack covered a large _____ in his search but did not find his lost dog.

B. Read each question. Draw a line to the word(s) with the same or almost the same meaning.

6. annoyed   a. certain

7. logical   b. researches or studies

8. unstable   c. reasonable

9. assured   d. not steady

10. investigates   e. upset

© Macmillan/McGraw-Hill

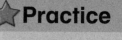
C. Write a word or words from the box to complete the paragraph below.

fossil	paleontologist	stumbled upon
reference	unstable	applauded

My brother Christopher wants to be a **11.** _____

when he grows up. He loves digging in the dirt to find buried items and

learn about them. He says it's like being a detective. One day, Chris

12. _____ something. It looked like a rock to me. He

explained that it was a **13.** _____ bone. Chris ran to look

in his **14.** _____ books to see what kind of bone it was!

D. Answer each question with a word from the box. Write the word on the line.

jumble	acquaintance	scuffling	disappointment	nutrients

15. How are you walking if you are dragging your feet? _____

16. What do you call the vitamins and minerals that help people stay

healthy?_____.

17. What would you call a messy pile of books and papers?

_____

18. If you are upset with yourself for failing a test, what are you feeling?

_____